INVENTORY 98

Missouri Wildflowers

by
EDGAR DENISON

*A Field Guide to Wildflowers of Missouri
and Adjacent Areas*

Revised and Expanded Fourth Edition

Kathy Love, editor

Cover: Pale purple coneflower (*Echinacea pallida*).
Jim Rathert, photographer.

Illustrations by author except where otherwise noted.

Preserve Our Wildflowers

Do not pick, do not dig!

The book has been donated by the author to the
Missouri Department of Conservation to further the
cause of nature appreciation and conservation.

**Published by the
Missouri Department of Conservation
P.O. Box 180
Jefferson City, Missouri 65102**

DEDICATION

To my parents who instilled
the love of nature in me, and
to my wife for sharing this
love with me.

E.D.

Contents

Introduction

In the monumental *Flora of Missouri* Dr. Julian Steyermark lists 2,369 flowering plants. Let us reduce this total by removing large groups of plants with specialized floral structures, the grasses, sedges, bur- and pondweeds. We further may eliminate adventives, brought in by railroads and trucks, and the occasional escapees from gardens and agriculture. Such introduced and escaped species have little chance of survival in this day of weed control spraying practiced by the railroads and the highway department.

The adjusted figure is around 1,500 species in 111 families. Even this figure should not scare the amateur because many groups (genera) have so many species that only an expert could possibly take an interest in identifying them; there are 50 different hawthorns, 20 kinds of asters, 18 species of tickseeds—to name a few examples.

Thus, we believe that the 285 plants pictured and the 454 described present a worthwhile selection of the state's flora, particularly of plants with showy flowers.

All plants shown and described in this book grow within the boundaries of Missouri. While the information on their habitat, distribution, and blooming time refers to Missouri, most of these plants can also be found in adjacent states. Thus the book should be useful to many midwestern flower lovers outside Missouri.

As a presentation of the Missouri Department of Conservation, the book fits into the Department's educational efforts to give Missourians a better understanding of nature's wonders and delights. It is especially hoped that these pages will find their way into the hands of young people.

Editor's Note: This revised and expanded fourth edition of *Missouri Wildflowers* features 17 additional species and 45 new photographs from previous editions. Mr. Denison has also added more drawings and simplified keys to make flower identification easy.

Many hands helped in the production of this fourth edition of *Missouri Wildflowers*. I am especially grateful for the technical assistance provided by George Yatskievych, Ginnie Wallace and Don Kurz, and for the many hours of production time from the capable hands of Bertha Bainer, Kevin Binkley and Mitzi Crump.

The Missouri Department of Conservation is deeply appreciative of Edgar Denison's contribution to the knowledge and protection of the state's abundant and beautiful wildflowers.

ksl

Wildflower Conservation

We have all seen a nosegay of wilted flowers thrown away along a field path, a sight encountered even in parks where picking flowers is specifically prohibited. A child—or a less innocent adult—was enchanted by the beauty of pretty flowers and picked them, only to see them wilt almost immediately. The idea that flowers are there for the picking is a mistaken one. It is one thing to "harvest" flowers which have been grown in gardens or nurseries and another when we deal with wildflowers.

An unpardonable loss of wildflowers is caused by teachers who demand plant collecting by their students and the preparation of herbaria by entire classes, leading to indiscriminate picking of whatever the student comes across in the field.

Our expanding population and the ruthless demands of our technological civilization take enormous amounts of land, destroying all life on it and endangering plant and animal species. Look at the huge number of houses and trailers which seem to mushroom in places that were forests and meadows only yesterday. Look at the devastation on our land through refuse dumps with discarded carcasses of cars, refrigerators, stoves, cans and bottles. Unguarded beauty spots, rich in flowers, become dumps overnight all over our state. Flowers disappear and we are poorer for it. Our society has not yet found the strength to deal with this disease and it makes every wildflower that much more valuable.

Under these circumstances every plant must be protected from destruction. The flowers serve many purposes. They are there to procreate the species, they serve as food to many valuable insects, they also serve plant-eating animals, and after dying each fall they become life-giving humus.

Because sometimes, in some places, certain plants appear in great profusion we are tempted to look on them as expendable. This, again, is an error, nature must not be disturbed willfully and cannot be disturbed without making our life poorer and duller. The wildflower lover will identify plants without picking them. Flowers are for all to enjoy—hopefully, for untold generations to come.

How to Use This Book

Arrangement by Flower Colors

The flower pictures are arranged by colors to make identification as easy as possible. Three factors make groupings difficult. First, flower colors are not always a pure color, such as blue or red or yellow, but fall somewhere between these, such as purple or orange. Second, individual plant species often have a wide range of color variations. And finally, the color definition is highly subjective. Like beauty, it is in the eye of the beholder.

The color groups are: (1) white and off-white; (2) yellow, cream, orange; (3) green, greenish-white; (4) brown; (5) red, pink; (6) blue, purple, lavender, violet.

A color index tab has been printed on the margin of the picture pages. The greatest problems with color fall in the lavender-purple-violet range, so cross checking will be necessary if you are having trouble with identification.

Species With Color Variations

Many species flower in more than one color. Such variations are mentioned in the captions of the color photos and in the text.

Time of Blooming

Within each color group the plant pictures are arranged in order of their earliest recorded blooming dates in Missouri. This sequence must, of necessity, be approximate. Many plants come into bloom at about the same time, others have very long flowering seasons. Still others, with a distribution throughout the latitudes of Missouri, come into bloom weeks earlier near the southern border than they do in the north. The blooming season for each species is given in the legend beside the picture and in the text.

Habitat

The "habitat" (from Latin *habitare*, "to dwell") of a plant is the environment in which it either prefers or demands to live. Some plants have very precise habitat requirements for soil, temperature range, moisture, light or shade, competition with other plants, tolerance to summer droughts or winter winds, or other factors. Other plants will tolerate an amazing range of conditions and thus can be found in many places. The habitat description for tolerant plants can only be generalized.

Distribution

The distribution of a species is hardly ever a clearly defined one. Plants may appear and disappear in specific localities. Species distributions in this book are in part based on herbarium records, in part on field experience and in large part on reasonable expectations. Even so, it is quite likely that some species may at times be recorded in localities outside their shown range.

Plant Names

Most flower lovers insist on using common names of plants, which causes no end of confusion. Some species have a dozen or more common names (see *Houstonia*, page 273). Others, botanically unrelated, have been given identical names. Three plants from three different plant families are called rattlesnake master in Missouri. What a seedbed for arguments and confusion! To avoid the problem we have no choice but to learn and use the botanical names.

Every plant in this world can be precisely defined by two names. The first designates the genus (plural, genera), a group of closely related plants. The second tells the species—the individual, specific plants within the genus.

Botanical names are Latin or Greek with Latin endings; this is called the binomial (two-worded) system. As the botanical names are frequently descriptive, the text includes a translation, though authorities are not always in agreement as to the exact meaning. Many species names honor botanists or refer to American states (*pennsylvanicus, ohioensis, missouriensis*) in which the plants, shipped to Europe for classification, had been collected.

Arrangement of Text

While the pictures are arranged by color and flowering time, the text appears alphabetically by scientific family name. The families are in two groups: those which have one seedleaf (monocotyledons) and those with two (dicotyledons). The Composite Family (*Asteraceae*) has been subdivided into three subgroups based on their floral arrangement.

Plant Families

The botanical text includes pertinent information concerning 66 plant families represented in this book. "Families" are created by botanists to bring some order into the bewildering confusion about 250,000 plant species worldwide. Described are: 1) distribution of a family in the world; 2) the worldwide number of genera and species; 3) plant and floral characteristics; 4) economically and horticulturally important members of a family; and 5) occurrence in Missouri.

The number of genera and species quoted by different authors varies unbelievably, depending on when a book was published, inclusion or exclusion of genera and families, and the determination of what an author accepts as a "species."

Worldwide data used here are based on the 1978 American edition of a British book, *Flowering Plants of the World,* edited by V.H. Heywood and published by Mayflower, New York.

Basic Botanical Terms

For other terms, consult the glossary, page 297.

The appearance of plants, their leaves, flowers, floral arrangement, flowering season and habitat give the clues by which we try to identify them.

LEAVES: are either simple or compound. They vary in shape and the appearance of the margins. Veination is netted, pinnate, palmate or parallel. Monocots (plants with one seed leaf) are parallel. There are a few exceptions to this rule.

STIPULES: are small leaflike appendages at the base of leaves or leaf-stalk. Often two (sometimes united) on each side of the leaf insertions.

BRACTS: are the modified or reduced leaf or leaves beneath a flower or inflorescence. In the Composites, a row or rows of leaflets forming the involucre.

FLOWERS: are either regular or irregular. A "regular" flower cut along any axis will present like sections. The "irregular" flower can be cut usually only along one axis to show like sections (bilateral symmetry), or it may be totally asymmetrical.

Types of Inflorescences

An inflorescence is the arrangement of flowers on a stem or axis. A **peduncle** is the stalk of a flower cluster or inflorescence, while a **pedicel** is the stalk of a single flower, fruit, leaf, etc.

TERMINAL FLOWER: The inflorescence is carried at the tip of the stem(s).

AXILLARY FLOWER: Flowers, either with or without pedicels, arise from leaf-joints. Stipules may or may not be present.

SPIKE: Flowers without pedicels emerge from a more or less elongated axis. Flowering begins at the bottom.

RACEME: Flowers on pedicels, which arise from a more or less elongated axis, the peduncle. Flowering begins at bottom.

CORYMB: A flat-topped or convex open inflorescence. The pedicels of varying length. If the inflorescence consists of only one peduncle, it is a "simple corymb," if several peduncles combine to form the inflorescence, it becomes a "compound corymb."

CYME: A flower cluster in which the central or terminal flower opens first.

UMBEL: A flat-topped or convex inflorescence, consisting of many small flowers, each on a pedicel. The pedicels arise from one point.

PANICLE: An inflorescence with a branched main axis, the branches bearing loose clusters of flowers.

4

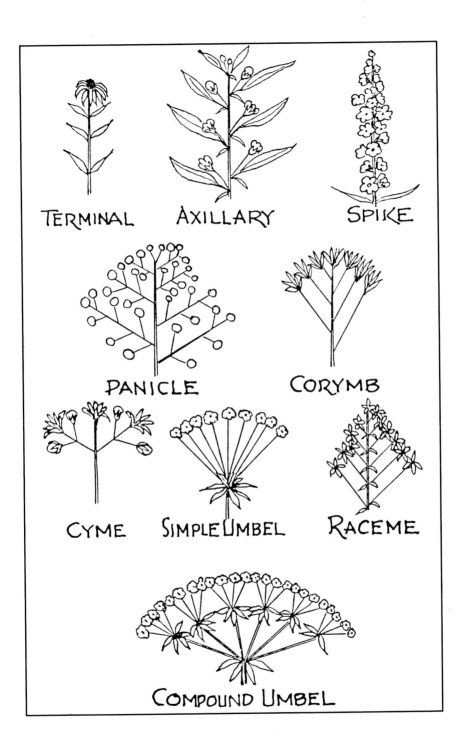

TERMINAL AXILLARY SPIKE

PANICLE CORYMB

CYME SIMPLE UMBEL RACEME

COMPOUND UMBEL

5

Simple Leaf

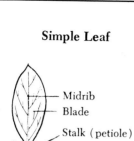

— Midrib
— Blade
— Stalk (petiole)
— Stipule (often absent)

Leaf Veining

Parallel   Pinnate

Compound Leaves

1   2

3   4

1. Pinnate
2. Twice pinnate
3. Palmate
4. Three-divided
   (trifoliate)
5. Three-times-three-divided
   (ternate)

5

Leaf Positions

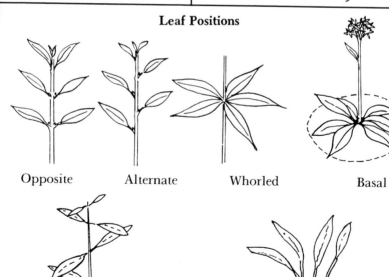

Opposite   Alternate   Whorled   Basal

Opposite (dessucate)   Basal (from root)

6

Leaf Shapes

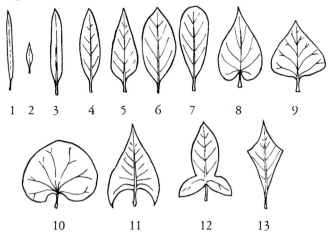

1 2 3 4 5 6 7 8 9

10 11 12 13

1. Needle-shaped (acicular)
2. Awl-shaped (subulate)
3. Linear
4. Oblong
5. Lance-shaped (lanceolate)
6. Ovate
7. Spoon-shaped (spatulate)

8. Heart-shaped (cordate)
9. Triangular (deltoid)
10. Kidney-shaped (reniform)
11. Arrow-shaped (sagittate)
12. Halberd-shaped (hastate)
13. Wedge-shaped (cuneate)

Leaf Margins

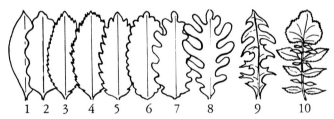

1 2 3 4 5 6 7 8 9 10

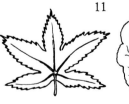

11

1. Entire
2. Wavy (undulate)
3. Toothed (serrate)
4. Double toothed (double serrate)
5. Coarsely toothed (dentate)
6. Rounded toothed (crenate)
7. Lobed
8. Parted
9. Incised
10. Pinnately (like a feather) divided
11. Palmately (like a hand) divided

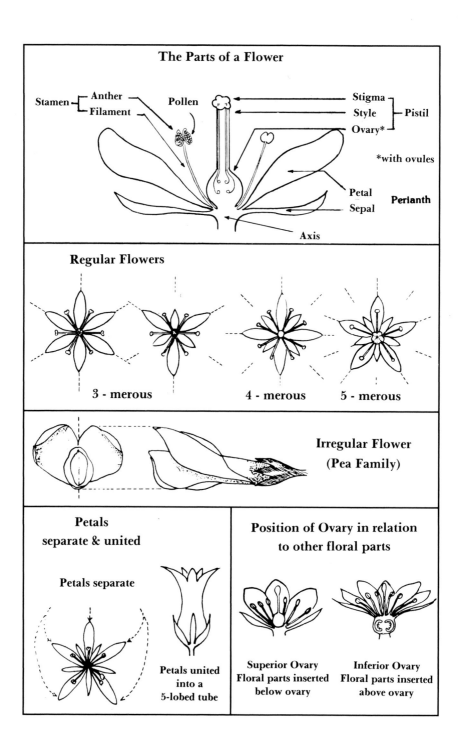

The Parts of a Flower

Stamen — Anther
— Filament

Pollen

Stigma —
Style — Pistil
Ovary* —

*with ovules

Petal
Sepal   **Perianth**

Axis

Regular Flowers

3 - merous   4 - merous   5 - merous

Irregular Flower
(Pea Family)

Petals
separate & united

Petals separate

Petals united
into a
5-lobed tube

Position of Ovary in relation
to other floral parts

Superior Ovary
Floral parts inserted
below ovary

Inferior Ovary
Floral parts inserted
above ovary

Plant Family Characteristics for Field Identification

Amateur botanists expect family descriptions to be a matter of clear and crisp definitions with sharp boundaries between families. This, unfortunately, is not the case. An authority on taxonomy, George H.T. Lawrence, wrote that "the family . . . is composed of one or more genera whose similarities are greater than their differences"—not an encouraging statement. Some families lend themselves to rather simple descriptions, but others are mixtures of many features which must be fitted together like pieces of a puzzle.

Few people memorize all the features of the 111 families with which we deal. Even if this feat is accomplished, it is of little value for field identification, because so many characteristics can only be found through dissection and the use of the microscope.

In the introduction we suggested that we are dealing in Missouri with 111 plant families and some 1,500 species. Surprisingly, nearly 80 percent of these are members of only 24 families. It is therefore very helpful for field identification to be able to recognize the family characteristics of these 24 families. The following tables attempt to provide the information for this task. Once the family association has been established, genus and species recognition will be much easier.

The tables are organized by floral appearance:
Floral parts are arranged in: 1) threes or multiples thereof;
2) four petals or lobes, regular flowers;
3) five petals or lobes, regular flowers;
4) five petals or lobes, irregular flowers;
5) special floral arrangements.

The characteristics given in the following tables apply to plants found in Missouri.

PLANT FAMILY CHARACTERISTICS

FAMILY	PETALS OR LOBES	SEPALS	STAMENS	OVARY, PISTIL
MONOCOTYLEDON FAMILIES—parallel-veined leaves, flowers 3-merous				
Liliaceae Lily Figure 1, p. 18	3 petals	3	6	ovary superior
Iridaceae Iris Figure 2, p. 18	3 petals	3	3	ovary inferior
Commelinaceae Spiderwort Figure 3, p. 18	3 petals often rounded	3 green	6 (Note 1)	ovary superior
Orchidaceae Orchid Figure 4, p. 18	3 petals sometimes difficult to recognize (Note 3)	3 sometimes 2 are joined or "fused"	1 or 2 attached to style (Note 3)	ovary inferior
DICOTYLEDON FAMILIES—arranged according to basic floral appearance				
REGULAR FLOWERS WITH 4 PETALS OR LOBES				
Brassicaceae (Cruciferae) Mustard Figure 5, p. 18	4 petals in cross position	4 green	6 (Note 4)	ovary superior
Onagraceae Evening Primrose Figure 6, p. 19	4 petals sometimes connected to a long tube (Note 5)	4 often united to form a long tube	4–8 (Note 5)	ovary inferior stigma 4-lobed cross-shaped
Rubiaceae Madder Figure 7, p. 19	4-lobed corolla tube	4-lobed united	4 alternate with lobes	ovary inferior

FOR FIELD IDENTIFICATION

LEAVES	OTHER CHARACTERISTICS, REMARKS AND NOTES
mostly narrow, but wide in trillium	Petals and sepals often look alike.
narrow and long	In *Iris* genus, the erect petals are the "standards," the decurved sepals are called "falls;" in other genera petals and sepals are similar or identical.
form sheath around stem (Note 2)	1: Sometimes only 2 or 3 are fertile. The filaments often are hairy and highly colored. Flowers appear triangular in terminal clusters. They open in the morning only. Petals equal-sized in *Tradescantia*, while lower petal in *Commelina* is smaller. Color range: blue, purple, magenta. 2: Swollen nodes at leaf axils.
either broad elliptical & often shiny, or scalelike	Flowers strikingly irregular. 3: The lower petal becomes an enlarged lip or, in *Cypripedium*, a sac. Stamens combined with style and stigma form the "column."
alternate, with pungent, watery juice, often pinnately lobed or compound	4: Flowers in racemes. Usually 6 stamens, the 2 outer ones short and the 4 inner ones long (or sometimes reduced to 2). Typical of the family is the formation of seedpods while flowering continues. Seedpods contain either one seed or appear pea-podlike with many seeds.
	5: The exception is one species, *Jussiaea repens*, which has 5 petals and 10 stamens. Color range: light yellow, white, or pink.
opposite or whorled	All species have very small flowers. Color range: white and pink.

FAMILY	PETALS OR LOBES	SEPALS	STAMENS	OVARY, PISTIL
REGULAR FLOWERS WITH 5 PETALS OR LOBES				
Malvaceae Mallow Figure 8, p. 19	5 petals	5 united	many (Note 6)	ovary superior pistil compound
Rosaceae Rose Figure 9, p. 19	5 petals usually rounded standing free	5	many, usually protuding	pistil 1 or more (Note 7)
	These floral parts arranged *around* the ovary (perigynous) instead of above or below. (Note 7)			
Caryophyllaceae Pink Figure 10, p. 19	5 petals frequently notched (Note 8)	5 either separate or united (Note 9)	5–10	ovary superior
Polygonaceae Buckweed Figure 11, p. 20	none	5 petal-like often enlarged into membranes	6–9	ovary superior
Apiaceae (Umbelliferae) Parsley Figure 12, p. 20	5 petals	5	5	ovary inferior
Solanaceae Nightshade Figure 13, p. 20	tubular corolla with 5 lobes	5 united	5 inserted in corolla tube	ovary superior
Boraginaceae Borage Figure 14, p. 20	tubular corolla with 5 lobes	5-lobed	5 inserted in tube alternate with lobes	deeply 4-lobed superior ovary; style single

LEAVES	OTHER CHARACTERISTICS, REMARKS AND NOTES
usually palmately veined	6: The filaments form a sheath around the style. The many anthers are clustered below the stigma. Flowers often showy. Fruit breaks into pie-shaped sections.
stipules sometimes winglike, at base of leaf-stems, (See picture on page 6, top left)	7: The ovary is surrounded by a cuplike structure, the hypanthium, on which the petals, sepals and stamens appear to be borne. The family is divided into 3 sub-families: 1) rose-subfamily, mostly herbs; 2) peach-subfamily, trees and shrubs; and 3) apple-subfamily, mostly trees.
entire, opposite, narrow, with swollen nodes	8: All but one genus with general distribution in Missouri have 5 petals, which frequently are notched. One genus, Whitlow chickweed, *Paronychia,* has no petals at all. Over half of the Pink Family species in Missouri came from Europe. 9: The sepals of some genera are united and form a long calyx. Color range: white, pink, red.
nodes swollen, covered by a sheath often with a hairy fringe. Sheath completely encircles stem & often is papery.	Flowers in slender spikes, some erect, others nodding. Color range: white, pink, greenish.
generally compound with sheaths at nodes and much divided	The tiny flowers form an umbel. *Eryngium* differs both as to inflorescence and leaf shape.
leaves and stems often prickly; leaves mostly alternate	Flowers, pleated (plicate) when in bud, are either star- or bell- or trumpet-shaped tubes of 5 joined petals. In the large genus *Solanum,* the stamens, united around the pistil, protrude beaklike from the corolla.
alternate, usually very hairy or rough (exception: Virginia Bluebells)	Flowers are positioned on a coil which unwinds as blooming progresses.

FAMILY	PETALS OR LOBES	SEPALS	STAMENS	OVARY, PISTIL
REGULAR FLOWERS WITH 5 PETALS OR LOBES (Cont'd)				
Ericaceae Heath Figure 17, p. 21	5-lobed corolla (Note 10)	5 united at base	8-10	ovary superior in *Rhodo-dendron*, inferior in *Vaccinium*
Convolvulaceae Morning Glory Figure 18, p. 21	5 petals (rarely 4) united into a tube twisted in the bud	5 (rarely 4) united at base	5 inserted deeply in the tube	ovary superior
IRREGULAR FLOWERS WITH 5 PETALS OR LOBES				
Scrophulariaceae Figwort Figure 15, p. 20	5 lobed (Notes 11, 12)	5 lobed	usually 4 with a sterile upper 5th (Note 13)	ovary superior
Lamiaceae *(Labiatae)* Mint Figure 16, p. 20	corolla with 2 lips (Note 14)	5 fused	4 (Note 15)	ovary superior
Square-stemmed plants are NOT necessarily members of this family.				
Fabaceae *(Leguminosae)* Pea Figure 19, p. 21 (Note 16)	5 lowest 2 often joined	5 united at base	many, often fused in groups	fruit a "legume," i.e., a pod, containing many seeds in a bean or peapod; fruit splits into 2 sections, seeds attached to one edge

LEAVES	OTHER CHARACTERISTICS, REMARKS AND NOTES
alternate	10: The two Missouri genera, *Rhododendron* (Azalea) and *Vaccinium* (Blueberry), have very different floral appearance. *Ericaceae* are indicators of acid soils. Color range: white, pink, greenish.
alternate	Trailing and twining vines. The flowers are only lightly lobed. Color range: white, pink, blue, sometimes with red throat. Fruit consists of 3 or 4 large seeds.
alternate or opposite or whorled	11: Most species have 5 lobes of the corolla, but the genus *Scrophularia* has only 3. 12: Flowers of most species have long, swollen, tubular corollas and are irregular, but others (e.g. *Verbascum*) have nearly regular flowers and the tube is very short. 13: As in the Mint Family, 2 stamens are often longer than the other 2. In the genus *Penstemon*, a 5th stamen is converted into a hairy stem without pollen-bearing organ (anther), apparently to attract insects.
most have square stems & aromatic green parts, opposite leaves	14: Flowers, either in spikes or clustered ball-like in leaf axils, 2-lipped. The upper lip with 2 lobes, the lower lip 3-lobed or divided. 15: The tube usually holds 4 stamens of which 2 are on long filaments and fertile, while the other 2 are on shorter filaments and either fertile, sterile or missing in several species. Color range: pink, white, magenta
generally compound with either many leaflets or with 3 leaflets (trifoliate) as in clover, alternate (but leaflets may be opposite) with stipules (see picture on page 21, figure 19) Some with tendrils at leaf tips	16: The family is divided into 3 sub-families: *Papilionoideae*—by far the most important sub-family, comprising most genera and species. Of the 5 petals, the lower 2 form the "keel," the 2 lateral ones are the "wings," and the large upper one is the "banner," "standard" or "sail." *Mimosoideae*—mimosalike tufts or balls of tiny, regular flowers. Two genera are widespread in Missouri: *Schrankia* and *Desmanthus*. *Caesalpinioideae*—flowers in this small sub-family are nearly regular as in the genus *Cassia* (senna).

FAMILY	PETALS OR LOBES	SEPALS	STAMENS	OVARY, PISTIL
IRREGULAR FLOWERS WITH 5 PETALS (Cont'd)				
Violaceae Violet Figure 20, p. 21	5, the lowest forms a spur (Note 17)	5	5 anthers form a cone-shaped cluster about the base of the pistil	floral parts attached around the ovary
SPECIAL FLORAL ARRANGEMENTS				
Asclepiadaceae Milkweed Figure 21, p. 21	5 (Note 18)	5	5 (consisting of 10 pollinia in genus *Asclepias*) (Note 18)	
Asteraceae (Compositae) Composite Figure 22, p. 22	Small flowers (called florets) are inserted in the expanded end of the flower-stalk, known as the receptacle. The receptacle is enclosed and supported by from one to many rows of small, leaflike bracts (collectively, the involucre). The florets of one receptacle are the "flower-head," of which there are three types: Note 19.			
Euphorbiaceae Spurge Figure 23, p. 22	The genus *Euphorbia* produces a floral cup, known as the cyathium. Inserted in this cup are male flowers and one female flower on top of a stalk (gynophore). After fertilization, the swollen ovary protrudes from the cyathium.			
Ranunculaceae Crowfoot Figure 24, p. 22 (Note 20)	none to indefinite	5 or more, often replace petals	many, arranged spirally	numerous, superior (carpelets)

LEAVES	OTHER CHARACTERISTICS, REMARKS AND NOTES
shapes very variable	17: Flowers of the genus *Viola* can be white, yellow, blue, purple, violet or mixtures of these colors. The genus *Hybanthus*, the green violet, has only one species in the U.S. See page 291.
leaves entire, opposite, whorled or alternate	18: See pages 145, 146 for details of genus *Asclepias*.
Very Variable	19: 1) Straplike ray flowers ONLY. 2) Disk flowers ONLY (NO ray flowers). 3) BOTH disk AND ray flowers. (See figure 22, page 22)
alternate, opposite or whorled	White, small petal-like appendages (usually 5) of the cyathium are common in the family. Only one native species of the genus *Euphorbia* has showy, white appendages of the floral cup, which simulate petals—*Euphorbia corollata*.
variable, palmate, often deeply dissected; basal leaves may differ from stem leaves	20: Flower shapes vary greatly: 1) Flowers with spurs or claws: irregular *Delphinium*, regular *Aquilegia*. 2) Flowers without petals, the sepals substituting for them *(Hepatica, Anemonella, Anemone)*. 3) Flowers WITH petals and sepals, normally 5 of each, but frequently more *(Ranunculus)*. 4) Flowers with petals and sepals, but the sepals drop when the blossoms open *(Actaea)*. 5) Flowers without petals whose sepals drop on opening *(Hydrastis, Cimicifuga, Thalictrum)*. 6) Flowers which are either staminate or pistillate *(Thalictrum)*.

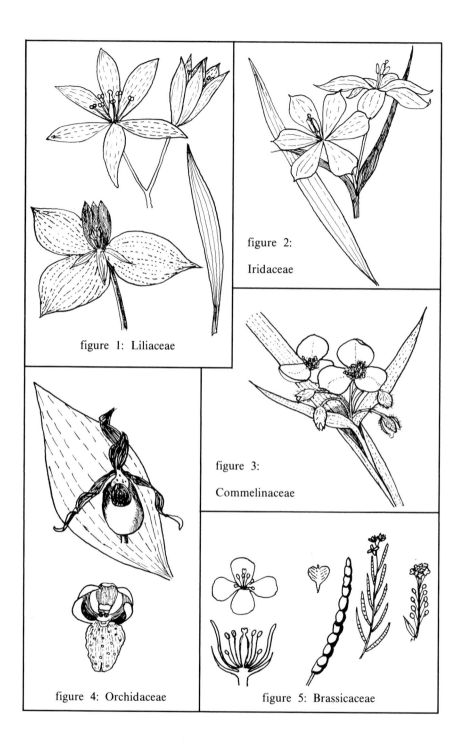

figure 1: Liliaceae

figure 2:
Iridaceae

figure 3:
Commelinaceae

figure 4: Orchidaceae

figure 5: Brassicaceae

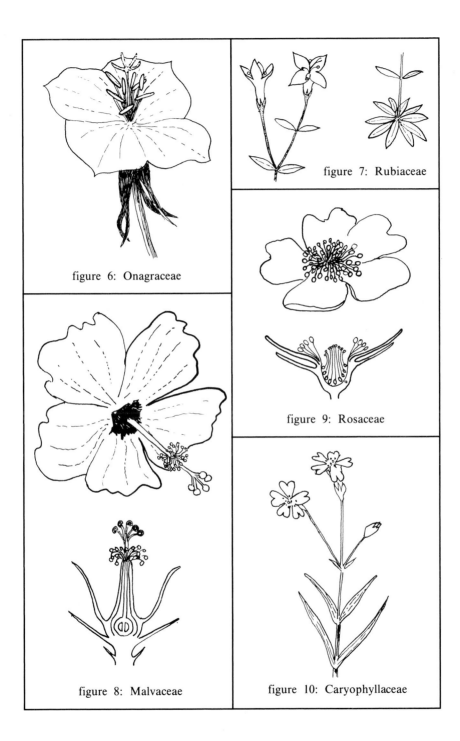

figure 6: Onagraceae

figure 7: Rubiaceae

figure 9: Rosaceae

figure 8: Malvaceae

figure 10: Caryophyllaceae

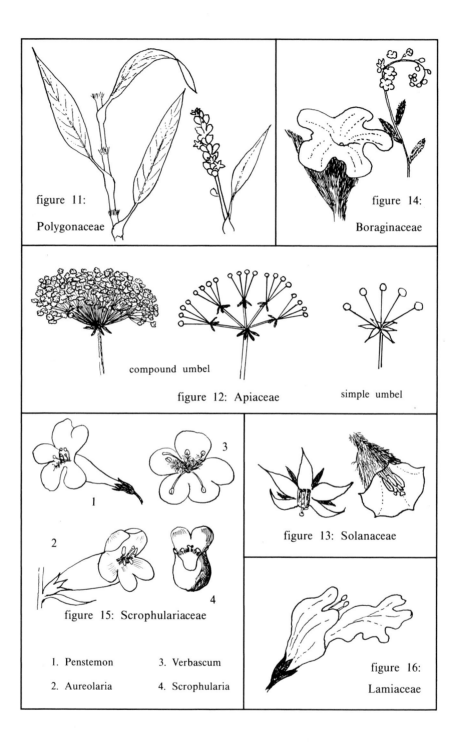

figure 11:
Polygonaceae

figure 14:
Boraginaceae

compound umbel

figure 12: Apiaceae

simple umbel

3

1

2

4

figure 15: Scrophulariaceae

figure 13: Solanaceae

1. Penstemon   3. Verbascum

2. Aureolaria   4. Scrophularia

figure 16:
Lamiaceae

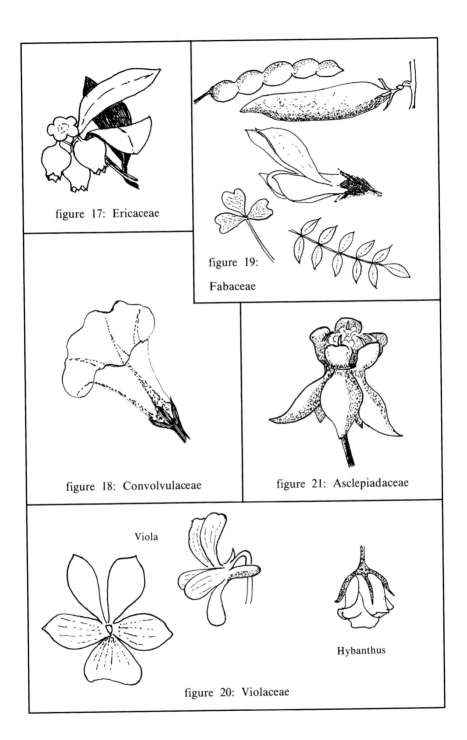

figure 17: Ericaceae

figure 19: Fabaceae

figure 18: Convolvulaceae

figure 21: Asclepiadaceae

Viola

Hybanthus

figure 20: Violaceae

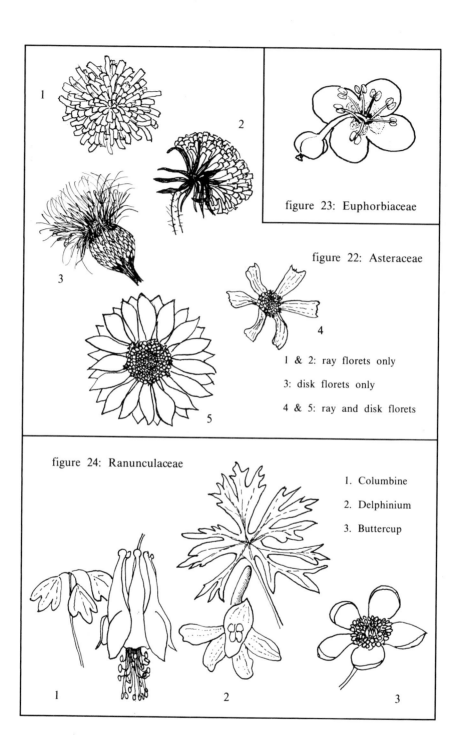

figure 23: Euphorbiaceae

figure 22: Asteraceae

1 & 2: ray florets only

3: disk florets only

4 & 5: ray and disk florets

figure 24: Ranunculaceae

1. Columbine
2. Delphinium
3. Buttercup

Erigenia bulbosa
Harbinger of Spring
January-April
Text page: 140

Saxifraga virginiensis
Early Saxifrage
February-June
Text page: 277

Wildflower Photos

Arranged by Color

Claytonia virginica
Spring Beauty
February-May
Also pink.
Text page: 254

Anemonella thalictroides
Rue Anemone
March-June
Also pink.
Text page: 258

Hepatica nobilis
Liverleaf
March-April
Also pink, purple.
Text page: 260

Isopyrum biternatum
False Rue Anemone
March–May
Text page: 258

24

Capsella bursa pastoris
Shepherd's Purse
March-November
Text page: 192

Comandra richardsoniana
Bastard Toadflax
May-june
Text page: 275

Valerianella radiata
Corn Salad
April-May
Text page: 287

25

Erythronium albidum
Dog-tooth Violet
March-May
Yellow—*E. americanum.*
Text page: 126

Dentaria laciniata
Toothwort
March–May
Also pale lavender.
Text page: 193

Dicentra cucullaria
Dutchman's Breeches
March–May
Text page: 221

26

Podophyllum peltatum
May Apple
March-May
Very rarely pink.
Text page: 187

Nothoscordum bivalve
False Garlic
March-May, also again in fall
Text page: 128

Amelanchier arborea
Shadbush
March-May
Text page: 265

27

Antennaria plantaginifolia
Pussy's Toes
April–June
Also off-white to pink
Text page: 156

Cardamine bulbosa
Spring Cress
March–June
Text page: 192

Sanguinaria canadensis
Bloodroot
March–April
Text page: 245

Lepidium campestre
Pepper Grass
April–June
Text page: 193

Prunus americana
Wild Plum
April–May
Text page: 270

Prunus serotina
Black Cherry
April–May
Text page: 270

Trillium flexipes
White Trillium
April–May
Text page: 130

Clematis fremontii
Fremont's Leather Flower
April–May
Also dull lavender.
Text page: 259

Ribes missouriense
Wild Gooseberry
April–May
Also greenish
Text page: 276

Erigeron philadelphicus
Philadelphia Fleabane
April–June
Also light pink.
Text page: 171

Anemone virginiana
Thimbleweed
April–August
Text page: 258

Nasturtium officinale
Water Cress
April–October
Also pale lavender.
Text page: 194

Cornus florida
Flowering Dogwood
April–May
Rarely pink.
Text page: 203

Viburnum rufidulum
Southern Black Haw
April–May
Text page: 199

Staphylea trifolia
American Bladder-nut
April–May
Text page: 286

Camassia scilloides
Wild Hyacinth
April–May
Also with bluish tint
Text page: 126

Osmorhiza claytonii
Sweet Cicely
April–June
Text page: 140

Houstonia longifolia
Long-leaved Houstonia
April–July
Text page: 273

33

Rubus flagellaris
Dewberry
April–June
Text page: 271

Crataegus
Hawthorn
April–May
Text page: 266

Fragaria virginiana
Wild Strawberry
April–May
Text page: 267

Plantago lanceolata
English Plantain
April–October
Text page: 246

Ornithogalum umbellatum
Star of Bethlehem
April–May
Text page: 128

Vaccinium stamineum
Highbush Huckleberry
April–June
Text page: 207

Hydrastis canadensis
Golden Seal
April–May
Text page: 261

Ptelea trifoliata
Hop Tree
April–June
Text page: 274

Anemone canadensis
White Anemone
May–July
Text page: 257

Smilacina racemosa
False Solomon's Seal
May–June
Text page: 129

Torilis japonica
Hedge Parsley
June–August
Text page: 142

Solanum carolinense
Horse Nettle
May–October
Text page: 285

Viburnum rafinesquianum
Arrow-wood
May-June
Text page: 200

Verbascum blattaria
Moth Mullein
May-September
Also yellow.
Text page: 282

Polygonatum
commutatum
Solomon's Seal
May-June
Text page: 128

Physocarpus opulifolius
Ninebark
May–June
Text page: 268

Convolvulus sepium
Hedge Bindweed
May–September
Also pink.
Text page: 202

Sambucus canadensis
Elderberry
May–July
Text page: 198

39

Lobelia spicata
Spiked Lobelia
May–August
Also light blue.
Text page: 196

Aruncus dioicus
Goat's Beard
May–July
Text page: 265

Kurz

Ceanothus americanus
New Jersey Tea
May
Text page: 264

Parthenium integrifolium
American Feverfew
May–September
Text page: 177

Datura stramonium
Jimson Weed
May–October
Also pale violet.
Text page: 283

Ipomoea pandurata
Wild Potato Vine
May–September
Also light purple or rose.
Text page: 203

Geum canadense
White Avens
May–October
Also light pink.
Text page: 267

Gillenia stipulata
Indian Physic
May–July
Text page: 268

Robinia pseudo-acacia
Black Locust
May–June
Text page: 219

Penstemon digitalis
Beard-tongue
May–July
Text page: 281

Verbena simplex
Narrow-leaved Vervain
May–September
Also light violet.
Text page: 290

Cornus obliqua
Swamp Dogwood
May–July
Text page: 205

43

Daucus carota
Queen Anne's Lace
May–October
Also pinkish.
Text page: 139

Baptisia leucantha
White Wild Indigo
May–July
Blue or violet—*B. australis*.
Text page: 211

Hydrangea arborescens
Wild Hydrangea
May–July
Text page: 276

Achillea millefolium
Yarrow
May–November
Also pink.
Text page: 166

Chrysanthemum leucanthemum
Ox-eye Daisy
May–August
Text page: 168

Lippia lanceolata
Fog Fruit
May–September
Also light pink.
Text page: 288

Apocynum cannabinum
Dogbane
May–August
Text page: 143

Yucca smalliana
Spanish Bayonet
May–August
Text page: 131

Euphorbia corollata
Flowering Spurge
May–October
Text page: 209

Galium aparine
Bedstraw
May–July
Text page: 272

Actaea pachypoda
White Baneberry
May–June
Text page: 257

Kurz

Cicuta maculata
Water Hemlock
May–September
Text page: 139

47

Silene stellata
Starry Campion
June–September
Text page: 201

Veronicastrum virginicum
Culver's-root
June–September
Text page: 283

Polymnia canadensis
Leaf-cup
May–October
Text page: 178

48

Cacalia atriplicifolia
Pale Indian Plantain
June–September
Text page: 156

Gaura biennis
Gaura
June–October
Pink when fading.
Text page: 241

Cephalanthus occidentalis
Buttonbush
June–September
Text page: 272

Pycnanthemum tenuifolium
Slender Mountain Mint
June–September
Also light lavender.
Text page: 233

Laportea canadensis
Wood Nettle
June–August
Text page: 287

Polygonum scandens
Climbing False Buckwheat
July–November
Text page: 251

Eupatorium rugosum
White Snakeroot
July–October
Text page: 161

Monotropa uniflora
Indian Pipe
August–October
Text page: 256

Reagan

Aster pilosus
White Heath Aster
August-November
Also purplish.
Text page: 167

51

Verbesina virginica
White Crown-beard
August–October
Text page: 185

Cynanchum laeve
Angle-pod
July–September
Text page: 150

Spiranthes cernua
Ladies' Tresses
August–November
Text page: 133

Eupatorium altissimum
Tall Thoroughwort
August–October
Text page: 161

Elephantopus carolinianus
Elephant's Foot
August–October
Also light lavender.
Text page: 159

Ranunculus harveyi
Harvey's Buttercup
March–May
Text page: 261

Ranunculus hispidus
Hispid Buttercup
March–June
Text page: 262

Lithospermum canescens
Hoary Puccoon
March–June
Text page: 190

Lindera benzoin
Spice Bush
March–May
Text page: 236

Sassafras albidum
Sassafras
April–May
Text page: 237

Viola pensylvanica
Smooth Yellow Violet
March–May
Text page: 295

Hypoxis hirsuta
Yellow Star Grass
April–May
Text page: 120

Pedicularis canadensis
Lousewort
April–May
Text page: 280

Astragalus mexicanus
Ground Plum
March–May
Text page: 210

Corydalis flavula
Pale Corydalis
April–May
Text page: 221

Uvularia grandiflora
Bellwort
April–May
Text page: 130

Lonicera flava
Yellow Honeysuckle
April–May
Text page: 197

Brassica nigra
Black Mustard
April–November
Text page: 191

Barbarea vulgaris
Yellow Rocket
April–June
Text page: 191

Stylophorum diphyllum
Celandine Poppy
April–June
Text page: 245

ypripedium calceolus
ellow Lady-slipper
pril–June
ext page: 132

Senecio obovatus
Squaw-weed
April–June
Text page: 181

Kurz

Baptisia leucophaea
Long-bracted Wild Indigo
April–June
Text page: 212

Coreopsis lanceolata
Tickseed Coreopsis
April–July
Also greenish-white.
Text page: 169

Aesculus glabra
Ohio Buckeye
April–May
Text page: 225

Potentilla simplex
Cinquefoil
April–June
Text page: 269

Erysimum capitatum
Western Wall-flower
May–July
Text page: 193

Zizia aurea
Golden Alexander
April–June
Text page: 142

Oxalis stricta
Yellow Wood Sorrel
May–October
Text page: 244

Tragopogon dubius
Goat's Beard
May–July
Purple—*T. porrifolius*
Text page: 155

Pastinaca sativa
Parsnip
May–October
Text page: 141

Oenothera macrocarpa
Missouri Evening Primrose
May–August
Text page: 242

Heliopsis helianthoides
Ox-eye
May–September
Text page: 177

Melilotus officinalis
Yellow Sweet Clover
May–October
White—*M. albus*
Text page: 216

Campsis radicans
Trumpet Creeper
May–August
Text page: 188

Pyrrhopappus carolinianus
False Dandelion
May–October
Text page: 155

Krigia biflora
Dwarf Dandelion
May–August
Text page: 153

Opuntia compressa
Prickly Pear
May–July
Text page: 195

Lysimachia lanceolata
Loosestrife
May–August
Text page: 256

Hemerocallis fulva
Day Lily
May–August
Text page: 126

Thaspium trifoliatum
Meadow Parsnip
April–June
Rarely purple, brownish-
    purple
Text page: 141

Potentilla recta
Rough-fruited Cinquefoil
May–August
Text page: 269

Solanum rostratum
Buffalo Bur
May–October
Text page: 285

Asclepias tuberosa
Butterfly-weed
May–September
Rarely yellow.
Text page: 147

Nuphar luteum
Spatterdock
May–October
Text page: 241

Kurz

Impatiens capensis
Spotted Touch-me-not
May-October
Yellow—*I. pallida*
Text page: 187

Ascyrum hypericoides
St. Andrew's Cross
July–October
Text page: 228

Hieracium gronovii
Hawkweed
May–October
Text page: 152

Physalis longifolia
Ground Cherry
May–September
Text page: 284

Medicago lupulina
Black Medick
March–November
Text page: 216

Stylosanthes biflora
Pencil Flower
May–September
Text page: 219

Hypericum perforatum
Common St. John's-wort
May–September
Text page: 229

Rudbeckia hirta
Black-eyed Susan
May–October
Text page: 178

Verbascum thapsus
Mullein
May–September
Text page: 282

Verbesina helianthoides
Wing-stem
May–October
Text page: 186

Lotus corniculatus
Bird's-foot Trefoil
May–October
Text page: 216

ilium michiganense
urk's Cap Lily
ine-July
ext page: 127

Ratibida pinnata
Gray-head Coneflower
May–September
Text page: 178

Rudbeckia triloba
Brown-eyed Susan
June–November
Text page: 180

Ludwigia alternifolia
False Loosestrife
June–August
Text page: 241

Oenothera biennis
Evening Primrose
June–September
Text page: 242

Hypericum spathulatum
Shrubby St. John's-wort
June–September
Text page: 230

Nelumbo lutea
American Lotus
June–September
Text page: 240

Cassia fasciculata
Partridge Pea
June–October
Text page: 212

Helenium amarum
Sneezeweed
June–November
Text page: 173

Coreopsis tripteris
Tall Tickseed
July–September
Text page: 170

Solidago juncea
Early Goldenrod
June–October
Text page: 184

Chrysopsis villosa
Golden Aster
June–October
Text page: 168

Silphium perfoliatum
Cup Plant ;
July–September
Text page: 182

Silphium terebinthinaceum
Prairie Dock
July–October
Text page: 183

Sida spinosa
Prickly Sida
June–October
Text page: 238

Helianthus grosseserratus
Sawtooth Sunflower
July–October
Text page: 176

Helianthus tuberosus
Jerusalem Artichoke
August–October
Text page: 176

Helianthus annuus
Common Sunflower
July–November
Text page: 174

Cassia marilandica
Wild Senna
July–August
Text page: 212

Kurz

Belamcanda chinensis
Blackberry Lily
July–August
Text page: 123

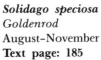

Solidago speciosa
Goldenrod
August–November
Text page: 185

77

Bidens polylepis
Beggar-ticks
August–October
Text page: 168

Helenium autumnale
Sneezeweed
August–November
Text page: 173

Aureolaria pedicularia
Fern-leaved False Foxglove
August–September
Text page: 278

Hybanthus concolor
Green Violet
April–June
Text page: 291

Euphorbia commutata
Wood Spurge
April–July
Text page: 209

Rumex altissimus
Pale Dock
April–May
Text page: 253

Vaccinium pallidum
Lowbush Blueberry
April–May
Also greenish.
Text page: 207

Heuchera richardsonii
Alum Root
April–June
Text page: 276

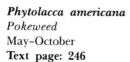

Phytolacca americana
Pokeweed
May–October
Text page: 246

Arisaema dracontium
Green Dragon
April-June
Text page: 120

Swertia caroliniensis
American Columbo
May–June
Text page: 223

Kurz

Toxicodendron radicans
Poison Ivy
May–July
Also nearly white.
Text page: 137

Vitis vulpina
Frost Grape
May–June
Text page: 296

Rhus glabra
Smooth Sumac
May–July
Text page: 135

Eryngium yuccifolium
Yucca-leaf Eryngo
July–August
Text page: 140

Thalictrum revolutum
Waxy Meadow Rue
May–July
Green, white, also light purple.
Text page: 263

Agave virginica
American Aloe
June–August
Text page: 119

Ambrosia trifida
Ragweed
July–September
Text page: 186

Asimina triloba
Pawpaw
March–May
Text page: 138

Arisaema triphyllum
Jack-in-the-Pulpit
April–June
Also all green.
Text page: 120

Asarum canadense
Wild Ginger
April–May
Text page: 144

Trillium sessile
Wake Robin
April–June
Variable color.
Text page: 129

---

*If you want wildflowers
in your garden
grow them from seeds,
do not dig them!*

Matelea decipiens
Climbing Milkweed
May–June
Text page: 150

Aplectrum hyemale
Adam and Eve
May–June
Text page: 132

flowers

Triosteum perfoliatum
Common Horse Gentian
May–July
Text page: 199

leaves

Scrophularia marilandica
Figwort
July–October
Text page: 281

Cercis canadensis
Redbud
March–May
Text page: 213

Verbena canadensis
Rose Verbena
March–November
Also rose-purple.
Text page: 289

Lamium amplexicaule
Henbit
February–November
Text page: 231

Hydrophyllum appendiculatum
Woolen Breeches
April–July
Text page: 225

Lamium purpureum
Dead Nettle
April–October
Also rarely white.
Text page: 231

Acer rubrum
Red Maple
March–April
Also orange.
Text page: 134

Castilleja coccinea
Indian Paint-brush
April–July
Also yellow.
Text page: 279

Geranium maculatum
Wild Geranium
April–June
Text page: 224

Dodecatheon meadia
Shooting Star
April–June
Also white.
Text page: 255

Monarda russeliana
Horsemint
April–June
Also lavender, whitish.
Text page: 232

Pyrus ioensis
Wild Crab
April–May
Also white.
Text page: 270

Rhododendron roseum
Azalea
April–May
Rarely white.
Text page: 206

90

Aquilegia canadensis
Columbine
April–July
Text page: 259

Oxalis violacea
Violet Wood Sorrel
April–July
Rarely white.
Text page: 244

Silene virginica
Fire Pink
April–June
Text page: 201

Asclepias quadrifolia
Four-leaved Milkweed
May–July
Also white.
Text page: 149

Lathyrus latifolius
Everlasting Pea
May–September
Also white.
Text page: 215

Tephrosia virginiana
Goat's Rue
May–August
Text page: 220

Mirabilis nyctaginea
Wild Four-o'clock
May–October
Text page: 239

Echinacea pallida
Pale purple Coneflower
May–July
Rarely white.
Text page: 170

Rosa setigera
Prairie Rose
May–July
Rarely white.
Text page: 271

Asclepias syriaca
Common Milkweed
May–August
Text page: 147

Asclepias purpurascens
Purple Milkweed
May–July
Text page: 147

Polygala sanguinea
Milkwort
May–October
Also white and greenish.
Text page: 249

Talinum calycinum
Rock Pink
May–August
Text page: 254

Lespedeza virginica
Bush Clover
May–September
Text page: 215

Oenothera speciosa
Showy Evening Primrose
May–July
Also white.
Text page: 243

Vernonia baldwinii
Ironweed
May–September
Text page: 165

Dianthus armeria
Deptford Pink
May–October
Text page: 200

Coronilla varia
Crown Vetch
May–August
Also white.
Text page: 214

Physostegia virginiana
False Dragonhead
May–September
Text page: 233

Blephilia ciliata
Ohio Horsemint
May–August
Text page: 230

Ruellia strepens
Wild Petunia
May–October
Rarely white.
Text page: 134

Schrankia uncinata
Sensitive Brier
May–September
Text page: 219

Anagallis arvensis
Pimpernel
May–September
Rarely white.
Text page: 255

Clitoria mariana
Butterfly Pea
May–September
Text page: 213

Sabatia angularis	June–September	
Rose Gentian	Also white.	
	Text page: 222	

Lythrum alatum	June–September
Winged Loosestrife	**Text page: 237**

Rathert

Dipsacus sylvestris	June–October
Teasel	**Text page: 206**

Echinacea purpurea	May–October
Purple Coneflower	**Text page: 171**

Cirsium vulgare
Bull Thistle
June–September
Text page: 158

Carduus nutans
Musk Thistle
June–October
Text page: 157

Petalostemon purpureum
Purple Prairie Clover
June–September
White—*P. candidum*
Text page: 217

Saponaria officinalis
Soapwort
June–October
Also white.
Text page: 201

Teucrium canadense
Germander
June–September
Text page: 235

Polygonum coccineum
Water Smartweed
June–October
Text page: 252

Hibiscus lasiocarpos
Rose Mallow
July–October
Also white.
Text page: 238

Lobelia cardinalis
Cardinal Flower
July–October
White very rare.
Text page: 196

Allium stellatum
Wild Onion
July–November
Also white.
Text page: 125

Cunila origanoides
Dittany
July–November
Text page: 231

Lespedeza procumbens
Bush Clover
August–October
Text page: 215

Phlox paniculata
Perennial Phlox
July–October
Also purple, white.
Text page: 248

Liatris aspera
Blazing Star
August–November
Rarely white.
Text page: 163

Liatris pycnostachia
Blazing Star
July–October
Rarely white.
Text page: 163

Desmodium canescens
Tick-trefoil
July–September
Text page: 214

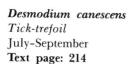

104

Perilla frutescens
Beef-steak Plant
August–October
Text page: 232

Aster novae-angliae
New England Aster
August–October
Variable colors.
Text page: 167

Agalinis tenuifolia
Gerardia
August–October
Rarely white.
Text page: 279

Houstonia minima
Least Bluets
March–April
Also white.
Text page: 273

Collinsia verna
Blue-eyed Mary
April-June
Also lavender, white.
Text page: 280

Viola sororia
Woolly Blue Violet
March–June
Text page: 292

Phlox bifida
Sand Phlox
March–May
Rarely white.
Text page: 248

Mertensia virginica
Bluebells
March–June
Also pink, white.
Text page: 190

Phlox divaricata
Wild Sweet William
April–June
Variable colors, rarely white.
Text page: 248

Sisyrinchium campestre
Prairie Blue-eyed Grass
April–June
Also white or yellow.
Text page: 124

Delphinium tricorne
Dwarf Larkspur
April–June
Also purple or white.
Text page: 260

Polemonium reptans
Jacob's Ladder
April-June
Text page: 249

Vicia villosa
Hairy Vetch
April–October
Text page: 220

Kurz

Specularia perfoliata
Venus' Looking Glass
April–August
Rarely white.
Text page: 197

Viola rafinesquii
Johnny-jump up
March-May
Also nearly white.
Text page: 292

Tradescantia longipes
Wild Crocus
April–May
Variable colors.
Text page: 122

Viola pedata
var. lineariloba
Bird's-foot Violet
April–June
Also lavender, white.
Text page: 291

Viola pedata
var. pedata
Bird's-Foot Violet
April–June
Text page: 291

Nemastylis geminiflora
Celestial Lily
April–May
Text page: 124

Cynoglossum virginianum
Wild Comfrey
April–June
Also whitish.
Text page: 189

Phacelia purshii
Miami Mist
April–June
Also whitish.
Text page: 227

Delphinium carolinianum
Carolina Larkspur
May–June
Also violet or white.
Text page: 260

Iris virginica
Southern Blue Flag
May–July
Also white to deep violet.
Text page: 123

Amsonia illustris
Blue Star
April–May
Text page: 142

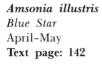

Tradescantia ohiensis
Spiderwort
May–July
Variable, rarely white.
Text page: 121

Amorpha canescens
Lead Plant
May–August
Text page: 210

Kurz

Justicia americana
Water Willow
May–October
Text page: 133

113

Prunella vulgaris
Heal-all
May–September
Rarely white.
Text page: 233

Echium vulgare
Viper's Bugloss
May–September
Variable colors.
Text page: 189

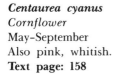

Centaurea cyanus
Cornflower
May–September
Also pink, whitish.
Text page: 158

Psoralea onobrychis
French Grass
May–September
Text page: 218

Commelina communis
Day-flower
May–October
Text page: 121

Cichorium intybus
Chicory
May–October
Rarely white.
Text page: 152

Verbena hastata
Blue Vervain
June–October
Variable, including white.
Text page: 291

Campanula americana
Tall Bellflower
June–October
Rarely white.
Text page: 195

Scutellaria incana
Skullcap
June–September
Text page: 234

Lactuca floridana
False Lettuce
August–October
Also nearly white.
Text page: 153

Lobelia siphilitica
Blue Lobelia
August–October
Also purple, white.
Text page: 196

Eupatorium coelestinum
Mist Flower
July–October
Text page: 162

117

Gentiana andrewsii
Closed Gentian
August–October
Variable colors.
Text page: 222

Without plants no animal nor human life could exist. Protect the plants!

Aster oblongifolius
Oblong-Leaf Aster
July–November
Text page: 167

118

Monocotyledons *Liliopsida*

Plants whose embryo has only one seed leaf (cotyledon). Floral parts in threes or multiples thereof. Leaves with unbranched, parallel veins (except in *Trillium* and *Arum* genera).

Amaryllis Family *Amaryllidaceae*

Worldwide in temperate zones with about 75 genera and 1,100 species. Flowers with three sepals and petals and six stamens. The 3-chambered ovary is inferior (while the similar Lily Family has superior ovaries). Horticultural subjects: *Narcissus, Galanthus* (snowdrop), *Leucojum* (snowbell), *Hippeastrum* (Amaryllis). Missouri has three genera with one species each.

Agave virginica, basal leaves; actual size 1 foot.

Agave virginica (83) American Aloe
June–Aug.

(Also known as *Manfreda virginica* and *Polyanthes virginica.* Put by some authors into a separate family, Agavaceae, Aloe Family.)

Habitat: glades, dry uplands, occasionally along streams in lime or acid soils; Ozarks north to Meramec River.

Flowers: a loose spike on top of a long, leafless stalk to 6 feet (1.8 m) tall; greenish, tubular with stamens protruding. Fragrance like Easterlilies.

Leaves: basal rosette, fleshy, dark green, lanceolate, pointed with fine teeth along margins. This is the only native Missouri representative of a large desert-dwelling clan.

Agave, Greek, "admirable."

119

Hypoxis hirsuta (56) Yellow Star Grass
April-May

Habitat: acid soils of prairies, meadows, glades, open woods; statewide except Southeast Lowlands.
Flowers: 3 sepals and 3 look-alike petals, bright yellow above, greenish and hairy below, with 1–3 flowers on a hairy stem to 6" (15 cm) high. Blooms often very close to ground.
Leaves: grasslike.
Root: corm.

> *Hypoxis,* Greek, (*hypo-* and *-oxys*) "sharp below," as the seedpods taper toward their base; *hirsuta,* Latin, "hairy."

Arum Family *Araceae*

About 110 genera and 2,000 species in the tropics, a few in temperate zones. Many small flowers on a spike (the spadix) sheathed by a leaflike bract (the spathe). The Asian *Colocasia esculenta* source of taro. Horticultural subjects: *Philodendron, Calla* and *Anthurium.* Missouri has three genera with four species.

Arisaema triphyllum (84) Jack-in-the-Pulpit, Indian Turnip
April–June   Also known as *A. atrorubens*

Habitat: rich woods; statewide. To 2½ feet tall, but usually about 18" (45 cm).
Flowers: tiny, on a clublike spadix. Preacher Jack in his "pulpit" enveloped by the canopylike spathe, which is either green or many hues of brown. Individual plants have either "male" *and* "female" flowers, the male above the female, or may have only male or only female flowers. It is reported that the plants can change these characteristics from year to year.
Leaves: on long stems, 2- or 3-divided, dull green.
Fruit: clustered berries turn from shiny green to brilliant scarlet.
Root: a starchy corm, poisonous unless fully dried. Indians ate them.

> *Arisaema,* Greek, *aris-* and *-haema,* "arum-blood," related to the *arum* clan; *triphyllum,* Greek, "three-leaved."

Arisaema dracontium (81)   Green Dragon
April–June

Habitat: rich moist woods; statewide. Occasionally to 3 feet (90 cm) tall.
Flowers: many, tiny on the lower part of the tail-like spadix, light green.
Leaves: divided into 5–15 lance-shaped sections (while *A. triphyllum* has never more than 3).
Fruit: identical to the jack-in-the-pulpit berries, see above.

Root: a flattened, round corm, often large, eaten by Indians.

dracontium, Latin, "of a dragon," for the long spadix.

Spiderwort Family *Commelinaceae*

About 38 genera with 600 species of herbs in warm, moist, temperate zones. Stems succulent with swollen nodes. Leaves with a closed, basal sheath. Flowers in boat-shaped bracts. Many used as garden and houseplants. Missouri has two genera with 13 species. *Tradescantia,* with eight species (of which four have very limited distribution), has three petals of equal size. *Commelina* (dayflower), with five species, has one of the three petals much reduced.

Commelina communis (115)   Dayflower
May–Oct.

Habitat: low woods, bottomlands, waste places, near dwellings; statewide. One to 2 feet tall (30–60 cm).
Flowers: emerge from a boatlike sheath, one at a time. Two large, blue petals above with one much smaller white or greenish-white petal below. Six stamens (the "male" parts); 3 on short stems are sterile staminodes, and 3 on longer stems (filaments) produce pollen.
Leaves: clasp the stem, narrow, lance-shaped.

The other species of **Commelina** in Missouri have similar characteristics.

Commelina named after Jan (1629–1692) and Kaspar (1667–1731) Commelin, distinguished Dutch botanists. A third botanist brother died young; *communis,* Latin, "common." Spiderwort from the spiderweblike hair surrounding the filaments.

Tradescantia ohiensis (113)   Spiderwort
May–July

Habitat: prairies, waste places, roads; statewide except extreme northwest and southeast. To 3 feet tall (90 cm).
Flowers: clusters with only one flower open at one time. Size of petals varies and flowers may be from ¾" to 1½" across (2–4 cm) in a triangular shape. Stamens bearded and fluffy. Colors blue, rose, purple, lavender or rarely white.
Leaves: about 12" (30 cm) long; narrow, folded lengthwise; bluish-green, clasping stems in a thick node.

Tradescantia named for John Tradescant, gardener to Charles I of England in the early 17th century.

Tradescantia longipes (110) Spiderwort, Wild Crocus
April–May

Habitat: wooded slopes and valleys with acid soils in the Ozarks. A low plant 6"-8" tall (15-20 cm).
Flowers: shaped as *T. ohiensis* with bright magenta, purple or purplish-blue colors.
Leaves: basal, grasslike but wide with a "crease" along center vein.

> *longipes,* Latin, "long-footed," possibly for the long leaves.

Tradescantia subaspera Zigzag Spiderwort
June–Sept.

Habitat: rich woods, bottomland, often near streams, generally on lime soils; central and east-central Missouri. To 2½ feet (76 cm) tall with many-leaved stems which change direction or "zigzag" between nodes.
Flowers: fairly small, light purple.
Leaves: dark green, to 8" (20 cm) long and 1½" (4 cm) wide.

> *subaspera,* Latin, "somewhat rough."

Tradescantia virginiana Early Spiderwort
April–June

Habitat: dry, open woods on slopes or in valleys, on acid soils of eastern Missouri. To 16" (40 cm) tall.
Flowers: many clustered in showy displays, though each flower lasts only one day. Flower appearance same as for *T. ohiensis*, with larger blossoms in blue, purple, magenta and related colors. On sunny days flowers close around noon.
Leaves: 2-4, to 5/8" (15 mm) wide, reminiscent of iris.

> Four other **Tradescantia** species occur in Missouri, all with very limited distribution. *Tradescantia* species hybridize, making identification sometimes difficult.

Iris Family *Iridaceae*

About 70 genera with 1,800 species worldwide in temperate and tropical zones, with major concentrations around the Mediterranean and in South Africa. Mostly herbs which store food in corms, rhizomes or bulbs. For floral details see page 10. Horticulturally important are Iris (German, Siberian, Japanese, Dutch, Spanish), Crocus, Freesia, Montbretia, Ixia, Sparaxis, Tigridia. Saffron is derived from Crocus stigmas. Orris root, an extract of iris roots, is used as a fixative in perfumes and cosmetics. Missouri has four genera with ten species.

Belamcanda chinensis (77) Blackberry Lily
July-August

Habitat: rocky, open woods and glades; statewide. Brought to this country by clipper ships, probably from China, it cannot stand competition and needs perfect drainage. To 3 feet (9 dm) tall and sometimes taller.

Flowers: in terminal cymes at end of branches, 1" to 1¾" (3-5 cm) across. The sepals and petals alike, orange spotted with crimson.

Leaves: nearly identical to those of the German garden Iris, long and broad.

Fruit: a capsule that splits open to reveal shiny black seeds, looking very much like a blackberry. Seeds remain attached for many weeks.

Belamcanda is a favorite in the yards of Ozarkians. The name is believed to be East Indian.

Belamcanda chinensis

Iris virginica (112) Southern Blue Flag
May-July

Habitat: wet meadows, swamps, river bottoms, ditches of northern and central Missouri, scattered elsewhere.

Flowers: near top of stems to 3 feet (90 cm) tall. Three sepals are descriptively called "falls," the 3 upright petals are the "standards." Colors variable from near white to deep violet, sometimes in a "veined" pattern.

Leaves: mostly basal, straplike to over 2 feet (60 cm) long.

Of the 4 native Iris this has the widest distribution; drainage "improvements" are eliminating its habitat.

Iris, Greek, "rainbow," because species come in many colors.

Iridaceae

Nemastylis geminiflora (111) Celestial Lily
April–May

Habitat: limestone glades and rocky slopes of eastern Missouri and a few western border counties. About 12" (30 cm) tall.

Flowers: a six-pointed star borne at the end of the branches, to 2½" (6.5 cm) across, blue-violet. Two flowers emerge from a common spathe (a bract) and bloom only in the morning.

Leaves: 3 or 4, very narrow, long and folded, clasping the stem.

Root: a bulb deeply underground, often in sticky clay. Though not common, sometimes found in large colonies on glades in the shade of junipers.

Nemastylis, Greek, "threadlike styles"; *geminiflora*, Latin, "twin-flowered" as explained above.

Sisyrinchium campestre (108) Blue-eyed Grass
April–June

Habitat: rocky, open woods, glades, roadways; statewide. To 2 feet (60 cm) tall but usually much lower.

Flowers: small, blue 6-pointed stars, variable in size, arising at ends of *unbranched* stems.

Leaves: basal, grasslike, stiff, upright, pale green.

Sisyrinchium, "a meaningless name of Greek origin" (Gray); *campestre*, Latin, "of meadows."

Sisyrinchium albidum Blue-eyed Grass
May–June

Habitat: eastern Missouri.

Flowers: white, otherwise identical to *S. campestre.*

albidum, Latin, "white."

Sisyrinchium bermudiana Blue-eyed Grass
May–July

Habitat: moist soils of woodlands and valleys; scattered statewide. Differs from the above by having branched, conspicuously winged stems.

Flowers: as under *S. campestre,* but pale blue to violet.

Leaves: deep green.

Lily Family *Liliaceae*

A large family of worldwide distribution with about 250 genera and 3,500 species. Most have swollen storage organs of bulbs, corms, rhizomes, or thick, fleshy roots. For floral arrangement see page 10. Food plants are onions, garlic, shallots, leek, asparagus and chives. An extract of *Colchicum* (wrongly called fall-blooming crocus) is much used in plant breeding. Horticulturally important are: tulips, lilies, squill (*Scilla*), hyacinths, troutlily (*Erythronium*), daylily (*Hemerocallis*, plantain lily (*Hosta*), lily of the valley (*Convallaria*), Colchicum, wake robin (*Trillium*), mariposa lily (*Calochortus*), yucca and many others with thousands of their cultivars. Missouri has 21 genera and 43 species.

Allium stellatum (102) Wild Onion
July-Nov.

Habitat: limestone glades and ledges mainly south of Missouri River, absent from southeast counties. Stalks to 12" (30 cm) high.
Flowers: umbels, 6-pointed stars on top of stalks, pink, sometimes white, showy.
Leaves: narrow, basal.
Root: all wild onions and garlics grow from bulbs.

All parts of the plant have a strong onion smell.

Allium, the classical Latin name for garlic; *stellatum,* Latin, "star-shaped."

Allium canadense Wild Garlic
May-July

Habitat: moist places; statewide. Eight to 24" (20-60 cm) tall.
Flowers: white, or, instead of flowers, little bulbs are produced which fall to the ground and root.
Leaves: on lower 1/3 of stalk, very narrow.

Allium mutabile Wild Onion
April-June

Habitat: prairies, glades, limestone exposures; absent from northern counties and Southeast Lowlands.
Flowers: variable colors of pink, deep pink, lilac, to nearly white, often showy umbels.
Leaves: narrow, basal.

mutabile, Latin, "changeable."

Liliaceae

Camassia scilloides (33) Wild Hyacinth
April–May

Habitat: prairies, rocky slopes, ledges, low, rich woods, absent from northeast counties.
Flowers: white to bluish white, fragrant, as many as 20 on long flower stalks to 2 feet (60 cm).
Leaves: basal, narrow, less than ½" (12 mm) wide, tapering to a point.
Root: a bulb which was eaten by Indians.

> The botanical name **Camassia** and the English "Camas" derive from the Indian word *Quamash;* **scilloides**, "like a **Scilla**" one of our early spring-flowering garden bulbs.

Erythronium albidum (26) Dog-tooth Violet, Trout Lily
late March–May

Habitat: rich woods, lowlands, along streams; statewide.
Flowers: white to bluish white on stems about 7" (18 cm) tall. Sepals and petals are nearly alike and recurve as the flower ages. Flowering is restricted to 2-leaved plants.
Leaves: to 6" (15 cm) long, elliptical, dull green with brown spotting and a silvery coating. In the East the plant is known as "thousand-leaf" as literally thousands of leaves cover the ground.
Root: a corm. It takes at least 4 years to raise a flowering plant from seed.

> **Erythronium**, Greek, "red-purple," the name of a European species which gave the genus its name; **albidum**, Latin, "white."

> A variety of the troutlily (**E. albidum var. mesochoreum**) is found mainly south of the Missouri River in dry places, glades and prairies. The petals and sepals do NOT recurve, leaves are narrow and without spotting, and the single leaves of non-flowering plants do NOT appear until after flowering and are few. Some authors give this troutlily species status as **E. mesochoreum.**

Erythronium americanum Yellow Dog-tooth Violet
March–May

Habitat: rich woods, bottomlands on acid or lime soils; scattered south of Missouri River.
Flowers: as *E. albidum* but yellow and a little larger.
Leaves: large, basal, elliptical and splotched brown.

Hemerocallis fulva (65) Daylily
May–Aug.

Habitat: along roads, abandoned homes, waste places; statewide. Native of Europe.
Flowers: 3 sepals and petals of dull orange color, the sepals slightly

smaller, terminal on branched stalks about 3 feet (80 cm) tall, spreading to 3½" (10 cm). Each flower lasts only one day.
Leaves: basal, narrow, straplike to about 2 feet (6 dm) long.

This immigrant was widely planted by early settlers. The plant is sterile and has spread from coast to coast by root divisions. Today there are thousands of garden hybrids but, strangely, none have been reported as escaped into the wild. Flowers are rich in protein and are eaten in China. The roots are said to taste like salsify. Neither insects nor diseases bother the plant.

Hemerocallis, Greek, "beauty for a day"; *fulva*, Latin, orange-yellow.

Lilium michiganense, whorl of leaves; actual length 10".

Lilium michiganense (71) Michigan Lily
June-July

Habitat: low woods, swampy meadows, along streams but sometimes on dry ground; statewide except Southeast Lowlands. Plant stalk 3–8 feet (9 dm to 2¾ m) tall.
Flowers: on stems arising from upper leaf axils, 3 each look-alike sepals and petals, orange with many purple spots; tepals recurve with the 6 stamens and the stigma protruding prominently.
Leaves: lance-shaped, the lower ones in whorls, the upper alternate, to 5" (13 cm) long and ¾" (2 cm) wide.
Root: a bulb.

This is the only member of the genus *Lilium* in Missouri. Some botanists classify this lily as *L. superbum.*

Lilium, Latin, the classical name for lilies.

Liliaceae

Nothoscordum bivalve (27) False Garlic
March–May

Habitat: glades, ledges, upland wooded areas, along streams, south and central Missouri.

Flowers: in an umbel on tall stalks without leaves, to 10" (25 cm) high; 6 tepals look alike, white or yellowish-white.

Leaves: basal, stringlike, lower than flowers.

Root: a bulb.

Though the plant looks like an onion or garlic it does not have the characteristic odor.

Nothoscordum, Greek, "false garlic"; ***bivalve***, Latin, "2-valved," referring to the bracts subtending the umbel.

Ornithogalum umbellatum (35) Star of Bethlehem
April–June

Habitat: fields, roadsides, suburban lawns, varied; statewide except southeast and northwest, but today probably in every county. Native of Europe, an aggressive colonizer, forming dense clumps of bulbs.

Flowers: clustered in umbels on stems to 12" (30 cm) high. The 3 sepals and 3 petals form an attractive star, often 3-cornered, white on the surface, with green lines below.

Leaves: grasslike, very dark green, rolled inward with a white center vein.

Root: bulbs produced at an amazing rate.

ORNITHOGALUM IS POISONOUS!

Ornithogalum, Greek, "bird's milk," an unknown liquid; ***umbellatum***, Latin, "in umbels," referring to the inflorescence.

Polygonatum commutatum (38) Solomon's Seal
May–June

Habitat: rich or rocky woods, streambanks, railroads; statewide. To 6 feet (1.8 m) tall but usually about 3 feet (90 cm).

Flowers: short floral stalks (peduncles) arise from leaf axils, each with from 1–3 small, tubular florets about 1" (2.5 cm) long, hang like bells, greenish white.

Leaves: sessile, broadly elliptical to 6" (15 cm) long with prominent veins.

Root: rhizome with many circular scars from the stalks of former years.

Fruit: dark blue to black many-seeded berry.

Polygonatum, Greek, "many knees," referring to the scars of the rhizome; ***commutatum***, Latin, "changing" (meaning unknown). "Solomon's seal" because of the seal-like scars of the rhizomes.

Smilacina racemosa (37) False Solomon's Seal, False Spikenard
May-June

Habitat: rich woods; statewide. Stalk is arching, 2-3 feet (60-90 cm) tall, usually unbranched, with a zigzag effect between leaf nodes.

Flowers: plumelike cluster of minute florets terminal on the plant stalk, white.

Leaves: alternate, spreading horizontally in two ranks, broadly elliptical, similar to those of *Polygonatum* (above) but with fewer veins.

Root: long, creeping rhizome.

Fruit: red berries with purple dots.

The flower arrangement of the true and the false Solomon's seals is so different that identification presents no problem.

Smilacina, Greek, "resembling Smilax," a large group in the Lily Family; *racemosa,* Latin, "flowering in a raceme."

Smilacina racemosa, fruit; actual length 9".

Trillium sessile (85) Wake Robin, Trillium
April-June

Habitat: wooded slopes and bottomlands in rich soil; common south of Missouri River, scattered north of it.

Flowers: one to a plant, arising stemless from a whorl of leaves. Colors very variable: brown, brown-purple, maroon, brick-red, brownish yellow, greenish yellow, greenish or a mixture with green. Three sepals and petals upright to about 2" (5 cm) high.

Leaves: 3 in a whorl topping a bare stalk of 8-12" (20-30 cm), ovate, pointed, sessile, dark green with or without gray mottling.

Root: short rhizome.

Fruit: many-seeded berries.

Trillium, Latin, "3" and "lily"; *sessile,* Latin, "without a stalk."

Liliaceae

Trillium recurvatum Purple Trillium
April–May

Habitat: rich woods in eastern and southern Missouri.
Flowers: very similar to *T. sessile*, but the sepals recurve downward as the flower opens.
Leaves: also very similar to *T. sessile* but they have a distinct, short stem.

This is the most commonly found Trillium in eastern Missouri; *recurvatum*, Latin, "recurved."

Trillium flexipes (30) White Wake Robin, White Trillium
April–May

Habitat: rich, wooded slopes and bottomlands, ravines; generally on east- or north-facing hills. To 2 feet (60 cm) tall.
Flowers: large, triangular, white petals. The 3 narrow sepals are green. Flower to 2½" (6.5 cm) across on a stem, either horizontal or drooping when in bloom.
Leaves: 3 heart-shaped, pointed, large in a whorl, usually as broad as long, to 9" (23 cm), green but not mottled.

flexipes, Latin, "flexible" or "bending foot," probably referring to the nodding flower.

Trillium viride Green Trillium
April–May

Habitat: wooded slopes or in full sun in valleys of southwest and east-central Missouri. Stalks to 20" (50 cm) high.
Flowers: sepals spread outward, petals erect to 3" (8 cm) long, green or yellow.
Leaves: sessile, broadly lanceolate or nearly round, green or mottled.

viride, Latin, "green."

Uvularia grandiflora (57) Bellwort
April–May

Habitat: rich, wooded slopes; statewide except some southwest counties. Stems smooth, usually forked, to 2 feet (60 cm) tall with zigzag pattern between leaf nodes.
Flowers: nodding, yellow with 3 matching sepals and 3 petals about 2" (5 cm) long, terminal.
Leaves: perfoliate (completely surrounding the stem), broadly oval, hairy underneath, bright green.

Fruit: a capsule.

Uvularia, Latin from *uvula*, a small, conical body in the center of the human palate, which the flower resembles; *grandiflora*, Latin, "large-flowered."

Yucca flower (actual size) and Pronuba moth on stamen.

Yucca smalliana (46) Spanish Bayonet, Adam's Needle
May–July

Also known as *Yucca filamentosa* and *Y. flaccida*. Some authors put *Yucca* into the *Agavaceae*, the Aloe Family.

Habitat: roadsides, railroads, abandoned homes, gardens; statewide. Native to southwestern United States, introduced into Missouri. The stout, scaly flower stalks to 7 feet (2.1 m) tall, topped by a panicle with many flowers.

Flowers: cuplike with 3 sepals and petals, about 2" (5 cm) across, creamy white. Only one insect, the *Pronuba* moth can fertilize *Yucca* in the process of laying eggs into the ovary. The emerging larvae consume some seeds but not all. A Missouri entomologist, Charles V. Riley, discovered this interrelation between plant and insect.

Leaves: basal, stiff, narrow, sharply pointed, thus "Spanish Bayonet"; to 2½ feet (75 cm) long.

Fruit: a large, papery capsule with hundreds of flat, black seeds.

Yucca, an Indian name erroneously applied to the plant; *smalliana* for John Kunkel Small, 1869-1938, a botanical author.

Yucca glauca is a native found only in the northwestern corner and along the Arkansas border in Missouri.

Orchid Family *Orchidaceae*

A large plant family, with about 750 genera and 18,000 species (one author claims 30,000) worldwide except the coldest zones. Many are epiphytic, living without soil, attached to trees and vines. Terrestrial species (those in soil) exist only in the presence of specific microorganisms in a symbiotic relationship. A tropical species, *Vanilla planifolia*, is source of vanillin. The breeding and selling of thousands of hybrids is big business. All Missouri species are terrestrial; there are 34 species in 15 genera.

Aplectrum hyemale (86) Adam and Eve, Putty Root
May–June

Habitat: bottomlands of rich, wooded slopes, often along streams in east-central and southern Missouri, scattered elsewhere.

Flowers: 7–15 on a bare stem to 12" (30 cm) tall, light to dark brown, sometimes slightly purple toward base of the 3 sepals and petals. Lip small, white.

Leaves: 1 or 2 per plant. They appear in September and disappear by flowering time. They are to 8" (20 cm) long with many white veins on a dark green background and often plaited underneath. This plant reverses the normal seasonal cycle of chlorophyll production by having leaves only in fall and winter with tolerance for subzero temperatures.

Aplectrum, Greek, "without a spur"; *hyemale*, Latin, "in winter" (referring to the leaves).

Cypripedium calceolus (59) Yellow Lady-Slipper
April–June

Habitat: upper and middle elevations of wooded slopes facing north or east in acid soils; statewide.

Flowers: variety *parviflorum* (small-flowered) in western and southern counties, a larger variety, *pubescens* (hairy) to 2 feet (60 cm) tall in eastern Missouri. The long, brown, twisted "flags," one upright, the other 2 on either side of the "slipper" are sepals. The bright yellow "slipper" is a modified petal. To achieve pollination, insects (mostly bees) are forced to follow a labyrinthine obstacle course.

Leaves: broad, prominently parallel-veined, clasp the stem, to 6" (15 cm) long, sharply pointed, hairy.

Cypri-, Greek for Cypris, the counterpart of Venus, *-pedium*, Greek, "shoe"; *calceolus*, Latin, "with a spur."

Spiranthes cernua (53) Ladies' Tresses
Aug.-Nov.

Habitat: limestone glades, upland dry prairies, wet meadows, south of Missouri River, scattered north.

Flowers: on stems to 18" (45 cm) high, white with a pointed lip, arranged in a spiral, about 1/3" (8 mm) long. Usually with a lily of the valley fragrance.

Leaves: few, very narrow, clasping the flowering stem. Basal leaves have disappeared before the flowers appear.

Spiranthes, Greek, "coil-flower"; *cernua,* Latin, "nodding."

There are 5 other *Spiranthes* species found in Missouri, similar to the above; one flowering in May and June, the others in late summer and fall.

Dicotyledons *Magnoliopsida*

Plants whose embryo has 2 seed leaves—cotyledons. Flower parts are usually in fours or fives or multiples thereof. Leaves usually have a network of branching veins.

Acanthus Family *Acanthaceae*

Mostly tropical shrubs with a few species in temperate regions, of about 250 genera and 2,500 species. Flowers usually irregular, 2-lipped with fused petals; stamens 2-4, several are often reduced and sterile (staminodes). The *Acanthus* leaf is believed to be the model for the Corinthian capital of Greek architecture. Missouri has three genera and six species.

Justicia americana (113) Water Willow
May-Oct.

Habitat: gravel or mud-margins of streams, lakes, sloughs, ditches; statewide except northern counties. Much branched, shrublike, usually 12" (30 cm) tall, often covering large areas.

Flowers: clustered on stems (peduncles) arising from the upper branches; about 3/4" (18 mm) long with a notched upper and a 3-lobed lower lip, pale violet.

Leaves: willowlike, narrow, opposite, sessile (stemless), 3-6" (7.5-15 cm).

Bees and other insects are much attracted to the flowers.

Justicia named for James Justice, a Scottish botanist of the 18th century.

Ruellia strepens (97) Wild Petunia
May-Oct.

Habitat: rich open woods, streamsides, open valleys and moist uplands; statewide. Perennial, either single-stemmed or branched, to 3 feet (9 dm) high, either smooth or slightly hairy.

Flowers: few, arising from nodes near middle of stems, tubular with 5 lobes, very much like a petunia; lavender to lilac-blue, very rarely white.

Leaves: opposite, on short petioles, ovate.

Ruellia, for Jean de la Ruelle, a French herbalist, 1474-1537; *strepens*, Latin, "rustling," the sound of exploding seed capsules of the species.

Botanically, *Ruellia* is NOT a petunia, which is a member of the Nightshade Family.

Ruellia humilis Hairy Wild Petunia
May-Oct.

Habitat: dry areas, glades, open rocky hillsides, in full sun; statewide. A smaller and very hairy edition of the *R. strepens*, protected by a coat of dense, fine hair from evaporation in a hostile habitat.

Leaves: sessile.

humilis, Latin, "low growing" or "dwarf."

Maple Family *Aceraceae*

Trees of the north-temperate zone, centered in China, with only two genera but 100-150 species, depending on the authors. Leaves opposite. Flowers in earliest spring; five each sepals and petals, the latter often absent. Individual trees can have 1) "male" and "bisexual" flowers 2) "male" flowers only 3) "female" flowers only 4) "bisexual" flowers only. Of 13 maple species in America, Missouri has five, all in the same genus.

Acer rubrum (88) Red Maple
March-April

Habitat: bottomlands but also rocky hillsides and bluffs of south and southeast Missouri; with opposite branches.

Flowers: unfold before leaves. "Male" flowers red, "female" flowers orange.

Leaves: 3–5 lobed, coarsely double-toothed (serrate). Young leaves red. Winterbuds, twigs and fruit are all red.

An important "understory" tree of oak-hickory forests.

Acer, Latin, the classical name for Maple; *rubrum,* Latin, "red."

Cashew Family *Anacardiaceae*

About 77 genera and 600 species of trees, shrubs and lianas in tropics and subtropics with few species in temperate zone. Leaves of many species contain resinous poisons. Flowers usually of five fused sepals, five free petals and five or more stamens. The mango, pistachio and cashew belong to this family. Missouri has three genera: sumac (*Rhus*), smoketree (*Cotinus*), and poison ivy (*Toxidodendron*) with seven species total.

Rhus glabra (82) Smooth Sumac
May–July

Habitat: upland prairies, old fields, along roads and railroads; statewide. Smooth, hairless shrub, rarely a small tree, forming thickets by root suckers.
Flowers: minute, in dense, pyramidal clusters to 7" (18 cm) long, greenish.
Leaves: alternate, compound, with 9–27 leaflets. Leaflets lance-shaped, toothed, opposite, turning red in August.
Fruit: clusters of small berries (botanically drupes) turning from rose-red to maroon, eaten by animals and birds including wild turkeys. A pleasantly astringent tea can be brewed with the "berries."

Indians made flutes from the stalks and a dye from the berries; they used the tannin-rich twigs and leaves for treating leather and smoked the leaves.

Rhus, an old Greek and Latin name; *glabra,* Latin, "smooth" or "without hair."

Rhus copallina Winged Sumac
May–Sept.

Habitat: usually on acid soil, borders of woods, fields, glades; statewide. Very similar to *R. glabra* with exception of leaves.
Leaves: the leaf-axis is winged between leaflets, which have no teeth. Young branches and leaf-stalks covered with fine hairs.

copallina, the plant contains a copal-like resin.

Rhus aromatica Fragrant Sumac
March–April

Habitat: open woods, borders of woods, fields, glades; statewide. A low
  shrub (in contrast to the other shrub sumacs), to 4 feet (1.2 dm)
  tall, much-branched.
Flowers: appear before the leaves, small clusters, yellow.
Leaves: 3-divided, the leaflets oblong with wavy margins; pleasantly
  aromatic when crushed. The 2 lateral leaflets on short petioles, the
  center leaflet on a very short stem (in contrast to poison ivy, which
  has a long stem of the center leaflet).
Fruit: clusters of red, very hairy berries in May and June (poison ivy
  has small white berries much later in the year). Birds eat the berries.

aromatica, Latin, "scented."

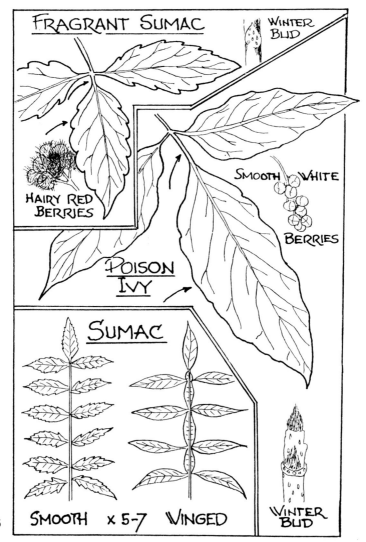

FRAGRANT SUMAC

WINTER BUD

HAIRY RED BERRIES

SMOOTH WHITE BERRIES

POISON IVY

SUMAC

SMOOTH × 5-7 WINGED

WINTER BUD

BEWARE OF POISON IVY!

The poison is a volatile oil, contained in all parts of the plant including the roots. Skin contact is either by touch or by smoke from a fire. After any assumed or actual contact, WASH exposed skin in any available water, preferably in hot water using soap or alcohol.

Do not confuse the leaves of poison ivy with fragrant sumac (*Rhus aromatica*) which has smaller, rounded leaves, the middle section being on a *short* stalk, or with box elder (*Acer negundo*), a tree whose seedlings look similar to poison ivy. Note: Box elder has *opposite leaves*; those of poison ivy are *alternate*.

Toxicodendron radicans (81) Poison Ivy
May–July

(Formerly known as *Rhus radicans.*)

Habitat: fencerows, open woods, roadsides, railroads, almost anywhere; statewide. Either a vine with aerial roots, climbing high into trees, or a shrub to 10 feet (3 m) high.
Flowers: in spikes arising from leaf axils, very small with 5 each sepals and petals, white or greenish white.
Leaves: 3-divided—"leaves of 3 let it be"—the 2 laterals on short stems, the middle leaflet on a much longer stalk. Leaflets (the 3 segments) large, wavy, ovate with rounded bottom, pointed to sharply pointed, with or without a few large teeth.
Fruit: white, sticky berries (botanically drupes) relished by many birds.

Toxicodendron, Greek, "poison tree"; *radicans,* Latin, "climbing."

Toxicodendron toxicarium Poison Oak
May–June

(Formerly known as *Rhus toxicodendron.*)

The terms poison ivy and poison oak are often both applied to poison ivy. Poison oak is a low shrub with oaklike leaves, never a climber, growing only in the southern-most counties near the Arkansas border and is not common there.

toxicarium, Greek, "full of poison."

Custard Apple Family *Annonaceae*

About 120 genera and 2,000 species of tropical trees and shrubs, with only a few species in the temperate zone. Flowers with three sepals and six thickish petals, several pistils and fleshy fruits, such as cherimoya, sweet sop, sour sop and custard apple. Missouri has one species.

Asimina triloba (84) Pawpaw, Missouri Banana
March–May

Habitat: wooded valleys, along streams in rich soils; statewide. An understory tree, rarely over 20 feet (6 m) tall, usually in dense stands from root suckers.

Flowers: appear generally before leaves; 3 sepals soon fall off, 6 petals in 2 whorls. The outer 3 petals overlap and recurve, the inner 3 almost erect. Petals, green at first, turn to deep purple-brown or maroon. Flowers' scent resembles fermenting grapes. Color and smell attract insects living on decaying matter.

Leaves: very large, to 12" (30 cm) long and 5" (13 cm) wide, smooth, entire, elliptical.

Fruit: oblong, 3-5" (7-13 cm) long, green, like a banana, containing a sweet custard in which large, oval seeds are imbedded; eaten by animals and humans. Late frosts frequently destroy the fruit crop.

Asimina, a French-Indian name; *triloba,* Latin, "3-lobed."

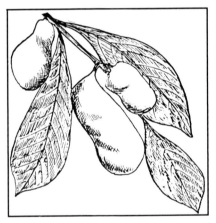

Asimina triloba, fruit; actual length 3½".

Parsley Family *Apiaceae (Umbelliferae)*

About 2,500–3,000 species in 300 genera, mostly herbs of world-wide distribution, especially in temperate uplands. Floral details, see page 12. Food and flavoring plants: carrot, celery, parsnip, parsley, dill, fennel, anise, angelica, chervil, coriander, caraway, lovage. Leaving out escaped cultivated species and railroad adventives, there are 25 genera with 37 species in Missouri.

Cicuta maculata (47) Water Hemlock, Spotted Cowbane
May–Sept.

Habitat: any wet situation in bottomlands throughout Missouri. A tall, vigorous plant with many leafy branches, usually streaked or spotted with purple, to 2 yards (2 m) tall. EXTREMELY POISONOUS WHEN MATURE!

Flowers: minute, with 5 petals, white, in compound umbels from 2–5" (5–13 cm) across, surmounting the leafy shoots.

Leaves: compound, the lower ones to 1 foot (30 cm) long. Leaflets linear to lanceolate, ovate with coarse teeth, but sometimes without them.

Cicuta, Latin, the ancient name for the true hemlock (*Conium*); *maculata,* Latin "spotted or mottled."

Daucus carota (44) Queen Anne's Lace, Wild Carrot, Bird's Nest Plant
May–Oct.

Habitat: fields, waste places, roadsides; statewide. Native of Eurasia. To 5 feet (1.5 m) tall, much-branched.

Flowers: minute, 5-petaled, white or rarely pinkish, in large compound umbels. The central floret on the umbel is usually purple. As the umbel withers it contracts, forming a bowl into which the seeds fall, thus the name "bird's nest."

Leaves: pinnately divided into straplike leaflets (decompound). A rosette of basal leaves is formed during the first year and overwinters. The flower stalk develops during the second growing season.

Root: a stout taproot, believed to be one of the ancestors of the cultivated carrot.

Seeds: oblong and spiny.

The plant is a troublesome weed, difficult to control. *Daucus* is the Greek and *carota* the Latin name for carrot.

Apiaceae

Erigenia bulbosa (23) Harbinger of Spring, Pepper and Salt
January–April

Habitat: in protected areas at the base of wooded slopes, along streams of Ozarks, southern and east-central counties. Plant starts to flower only 2–3" (5–7½ cm) above ground, but later reaches to 8" (20 cm).
Flowers: *Erigenia* opens the spring flowering season. Tiny, white florets in very small, simple umbels. Red-brown anthers show prominently, giving the name "pepper and salt."
Leaves: divided, fernlike, usually show sometime after flowering begins.
Root: a small, ball-shaped tuber.

Erigenia, Greek, "early-born," the name given by Homer to Eos, the goddess of the dawn; *bulbosa,* Latin, "bulbous."

Eryngium yuccifolium (82) Rattlesnake Master, Yucca-leaf
July–Aug. Eryngo, Button Snakeroot

Habitat: glades, prairies, rocky open woods; statewide except Southeast Lowlands. The inflorescence carried on a tall, straight stem to 4 feet (1.2 m) high.
Flowers: in dense, global heads (rather than in umbels), subtended by bracts. Flowers greenish, each with its own minute bract.
Leaves: yuccalike, the lower ones to 3 feet (90 cm) long, much shorter along the stems, bluish, linear, parallel veined, with small spines.
Root: an extract was supposed to be effective against snake poison, thus the name "snakeroot," given to many plants.

Eryngium from Greek *Errugion,* the name of a thistle; *yuccifolium,* Latin, "with the leaves of a yucca."

Osmorhiza claytonii (33) Sweet Cicely, Woolly Sweet Cicely
April–June

Habitat: rich wooded slopes or bottomlands; statewide except Southeast Lowlands. An herb to 3 feet (90 cm) tall.
Flowers: minute, white, massed on simple umbels.
Leaves: twice ternately compound (in 3 sections, 2 lateral, 1 terminal, all 3 divided again into 3 sections), coarsely toothed, the lateral leaflets on a short stalk, the terminal on a longer one; aromatic.
Root: like a carrot, highly aromatic with an anise or licorice scent.

Osmorhiza, Greek, "aromatic root," *claytonii,* for John Clayton, an 18th century botanist from Virginia.

Osmorhiza longistylis Anise-root, Sweet Cicely

Habitat and appearance same as *O. claytonii,* but the styles are minutely longer, a feature almost impossible to determine in the field.

Pastinaca sativa (62) Parsnip
May–Oct.

Habitat: fields, waste places, roadways, railroads of west, north and central Missouri. Native of Europe. Fleshy, much-branched stems, to 4 feet (1.2 m) tall.
Flowers: very small, light yellow, in compound umbels.
Leaves: compound, with opposite leaflets spaced well apart, with large teeth or lobed.

This is probably the same plant as the cultivated parsnip grown for its edible roots.

Pastinaca, from *pastus* Latin, "food"; *sativa*, Latin, "sown" or "planted."

Thaspium trifoliatum (65) Meadow Parsnip
April–June

Habitat: prairies, rocky open woods, ledges, bluffs. Common south and scattered north of Missouri River. Much-branched, to 2½ feet (75 cm) tall, without hairs.
Flowers: minute, in compound, flat umbels, dark yellow, rarely purple or brownish-purple. The central floret of each umbellet is slightly raised, a distinguishing characteristic from the very similar *Zizia* or golden Alexander (see page ??).
Leaves: the basal ones simple, heart-shaped or only once divided. Stem leaves on long stems (petioles) divided into 3 pointed, egg-shaped, finely toothed leaflets with a rounded base.

All leaflets have a very narrow yellowish-white margin, a ready identification characteristic.

Thaspium, a word play on *Thapsium*, another member of the Parsley Family; *trifoliatum*, Latin, "three-leafed."

Thaspium barbinode Hairy-jointed Meadow Parsnip
" -June

same as *T. trifoliatum*, as is distribution and general appea-
, but upper nodes hairy.
.ers: minute, in compound umbels, creamy or pale yellow.
Leaves: 3-divided, wedge-shaped, with long petioles and coarse teeth.

barbinode, Latin, "bearded at the nodes."

Torilis japonica (37) Hedge Parsley
June-Aug.

Habitat: waste places, roadsides, fields; statewide. Native of Eurasia. Much-branched, to 2½ feet (75 cm) tall with umbels raised well above foliage. Came to Missouri after 1900, spreading rapidly.
Flowers: on long stems (peduncles), white, in umbels, minute with 5 each sepals and petals.
Leaves: ternately once or twice compound, look like parsley.
Fruit: densely covered with hooked prickles which cling to clothing and fur.

Torilis, a name of unknown origin.

Zizia aurea (61) Golden Alexander
April-June

Habitat: moist localities in fields, open woods, glades; statewide. To 2 feet (60 cm) tall, often in large colonies. Easily mistaken for *Thaspium trifoliatum.*
Flowers: open, compound umbels, bright yellow, in a more or less flat-topped display.
Leaves: lower, twice ternate, upper once ternate or irregularly compound. Leaflets ovate, finely serrate.

Zizia, for Johann Baptist Ziz, 1779-1829, a German botanist; *aurea,* Latin, "golden." The common name "golden Alexander" refers to another member of the Parsley Family, *Petrosilium alexandrinum.*

Dogbane Family *Apocynaceae*

Mostly trees, shrubs and lianas, pantropic with few members in temperate zone. About 180 genera with 1,500 species. Closely related to Milkweed Family. Plants contain a milky juice, often poisonous. Flowers 5-merous with fused sepals and petals. Stamens inserted in floral tube, alternating with lobes. Important members of family: oleander, a poisonous ornamental shrub; periwinkle (*Vinca*), a groundcover; *Plumeria*, the frangipani of Hawaiian leis; *Rauvolfia*, Indian source of tranquilizing drugs. Missouri has two genera with seven species.

Amsonia illustris (112) Blue Star
April-May

Habitat: gravel bars, moist situations near bluffs and creeks in southern and eastern Missouri. A striking plant, forming clumps 18" to 3 feet (45-90 cm) high.
Flowers: cymes with many star-shaped flowers, the spreading lobes of the corolla, light blue with a delicate scent.

Leaves: narrow lance-shaped, shiny above. Swallowtail butterflies love the *Amsonias*, especially the zebra swallowtail.

Amsonia for Charles Amson, an 18th century physician in Virginia; *illustris,* Latin, "bright."

Amsonia tabernaemontana Blue Star
April–May

Habitat: rich woods, ravines, along streams (whereas *A. illustris* is primarily found on gravel bars). Mainly in southwestern Ozarks and scattered in eastern Missouri. Very similar to *A. illustris,* above, but leaves are dull on the surface.

tabernaemontana for Jacobus Theodorus Tabernaemontanus, the latinized name of Jakob T. von Bergzabern (Mueller), 1520–1590, the German author of a famous herbal, *Neuw Kreuterbuch (New Herb Book).*

Apocynum cannabinum (46) Indian Hemp, Dogbane
May–Aug.

Habitat: prairies, glades, waste places, roadways; statewide. Upright perennial to 3 feet (90 cm) tall with opposite branches.
Flowers: tiny, 5-pointed bells, massed in cymes, white or greenish white, very attractive to bees.
Leaves: opposite, smooth-edged, oblong or lance-shaped, with conspicuous petioles (stalks). Stems have a tough fiber-bark that can be used like hemp for making rope or tying. When bruised, all parts of the plant exude a white, poisonous juice which has been used for medicinal purposes.

Apocynum, Greek, "away dog" or probably "do away with dog"; *cannabinum,* Latin, "like hemp" as explained above.

Apocynum medium Intermediate Dogbane
May-July

Habitat: borders of woods, prairies, scattered; statewide. Believed to be a fertile hybrid of *A. cannabinum* and *A. androsaemifolium.* Differs from *A. cannabinum* having flowers white or light pink with spreading but not recurving lobes, and leaves which are sessile (no stems).

medium, Latin, "intermediate."

Apocynum androsaemifolium Spreading Dogbane
May–July

Habitat: dry woods, prairies, thickets, scattered through Missouri. Shrub-like.
Flowers: pink to white, marked with red inside, bell-shaped, the lobes spreading or recurved.
Leaves: many, drooping or wide-spreading, on stems, ovate to oblong lanceolate.

androsaenifolium, Latin, "with leaves of *androsaema.*"

143

Birthwort Family *Aristolochiaceae*

Only seven genera with about 625 species of herbs, shrubs and especially lianas in tropical and temperate zones. Flowers of Missouri species are irregular, tube-shaped and variable. Native species have no petals and stamens are united with the style. *Aristolochia serpentaria* is supposed to have medicinal use and is hunted by root-diggers. Missouri has two genera with three species.

Asarum canadense (84) Wild Ginger
April–May

Habitat: rich, wooded slopes, moist valleys, ravines; statewide except Southeast Lowlands and a few western counties. A low-growing, hairy plant, about 6" (15 cm) high, spreading from creeping underground stems.
Flowers: hidden by the leaves, arise from leaf axils, 3-parted, red-brown with stiff, white hairs. Flowers emit a scent of decaying fruit.
This and their color attracts certain insects essential to pollination.
Leaves: large, heart-shaped, strongly veined, leathery with shiny surface.
Roots: fleshy, intertwined, have the distinct aroma of ginger and were used as a ginger substitute in colonial times.

Asarum, Greek, the ancient name of the European species.

Milkweed Family *Asclepiadaceae*

About 250 genera and 1,800–2,000 species of herbs, shrubs, climbers and trees, mainly tropical and subtropical, but also well represented in temperate zone. Most species have a milky, often poisonous juice, opposite or whorled leaves, and 5-merous flowers. Stamens commonly united with the stigma in an organ called gynostegium. Pollen grains joined into a sacklike body, called pollinium. Seeds generally with long, silky hair. For floral details, see page 16. The large family has little economic significance. *Hoya carnosa*, the wax plant, is a house plant. Missouri has three genera with 20 species.

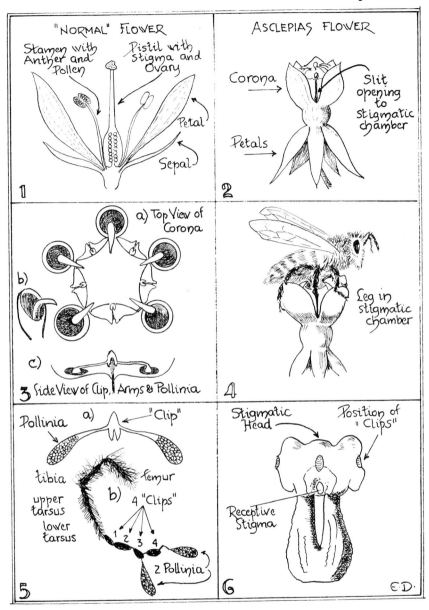

Asclepias, the process of pollination.

The genus *Asclepias* is represented by 15 species in Missouri of which 9 are widely distributed. All *Asclepias* contain poisons, but the monarch butterfly is immune to them and its larva eats milkweeds exclusively, retains the poisons through the pupa stage and passes them on to the butterfly, which, in consequence, is shunned by birds. Swal-

145

lowtails and fritillaries visit the flowers, though they are pollinated by bees and beelike insects. The seeds are provided with a silk floss parachute. The "silk" has been used as a kapok substitute. *Asclepias*, the Greek god of healing.

The floral arrangement of *Asclepias* is fundamentally different from what we visualize as a "normal" flower, and presents an evolutionary puzzle that is worthwhile examining.

a) The sepals and petals are usually turned downward (see 2) and are surmounted by the "sexual" organs and receptacles for nectar, collectively called a *corona* (Latin, "crown").

b) Looking down on the corona (see 3) one sees 5 nectaries, each with a protruding spur, called a "horn," though it is of soft tissue. This horn seems to serve as an obstacle for the insect gathering nectar, for reasons given below.

c) There are no stamens with filaments and anthers. But there are 10 pollen-sacks of fused pollen grains, called "pollinium" (pollinia, plural). (See 5a and 3c.)

d) Each pollen-sack is located in a silolike pocket (see 3c) and each pair of sacks is connected by a line, called the translator (see 5a). These connecting lines come together in a strange centerpiece, well-named a "clip" or gland (botanically, the *corpusculum*, Latin, "the little body.")

e) There is no pistil with a stigma at its top. But, below the anchor points of the "clips," there are 5 vertical slits opening into what is known as stigmatic chambers (see 4).

f) As a nectar-gathering insect alights, almost invariably one of its legs gets caught in one of those slits (see 4). The "clip" at the top of the slit attaches to the leg, and as the leg is pulled out—often with difficulty—the clip and the 2 pollen-sacks remain on the insect's leg. (see 5.)

g) On visiting another flower the same thing happens again—a leg is caught and in freeing it a previously acquired pollen-sack is torn loose and remains in the stigmatic chamber.

h) The pollen grains germinate, producing pollen tubes, which grow toward and into a minute opening in the side of the stigmatic column, the *gynostemium* (see 6). The large top-surface of this organ plays no part in reproduction.

Asclepias Key

1 a) Habitat: Upland fields, prairies, glades, wasteland, edges of woods.
flowers orange, rarely yellow . . . . *tuberosa*
flowers crimson or madder . . . . *purpurascens*
flowers flesh-colored, pink . . . . *syriaca*
flowers green with purple . . . . *viridis*
flowers all green: go to number 2
   2 a) leaves small, linear; flowers terminal on unbranched
     stems . . . . *verticillata*
   2 b) leaves narrow and long, flower clusters on short stems from
     leaf axils . . . . *hirtella*
   2 c) Leaves broad-ovate, flowers terminal AND in leaf
     axils . . . . *viridiflora*
1 b) Habitat: Moist, open bottomlands, floodplains
flowers pink, rarely white . . . . *incarnata*
1 c) Habitat: Open woods
flowers white or pink . . . . *quadrifolia*

Asclepias tuberosa (66) Butterfly-weed
May–Sept.

Habitat: upland fields, prairies, glades, wasteland, edges of woods, often
on disturbed soil; statewide. To 3 feet (90 cm) tall.
Flowers: massively displayed in terminal umbels. Many shades of orange
to brick-red, occasionally yellow.
Leaves: hairy, narrow, lance-shaped, dark green on very short stems.
Fruit: long seedpods to 4½" (12 cm) with numerous, tightly packed
seeds in spirals, released and windborne on their silky floss.

tuberosa, Latin, "swollen," referring to the root.

Asclepias purpurascens (94) Purple Milkweed
May–July

Habitat: upland fields, prairies, glades, wasteland, especially at the
edges of wooded areas; statewide except Southeast Lowlands.
Flowers: crimson, crimson magenta, but never purple, borne in umbels
usually on stout, single stalks.
Leaves: broad, ovate, pointed at both ends, with fine down on underside,
on very short stalks, to 6" (15 cm) long.
Fruit: as under *A. tuberosa*.

purpurascens, Latin "becoming purple."

Asclepias syriaca (94) Common Milkweed
May–Aug.

Habitat: upland fields, prairies, glades, wasteland, edges of woods. The
most commonly seen milkweed, especially in abandoned fields and
waste places; statewide.

Asclepiadaceae

Flowers: pink to lilac, very fragrant, borne in clusters terminally and along the stems, arising from leaf axils.
Leaves: broadly elliptical, rounded at base, to 6" (15 cm) long, fine hairs underneath, on distinct stalks (petioles).
Fruit: large seedpods, elongated with a protuberance.

syriaca, the plant was erroneously thought to be native to Syria or the Middle East.

Asclepias syriaca, seedpods

Asclepias viridis Green-flowered Milkweed
May–July

Habitat: primarily on glades south of the Missouri River. Plant to 2 feet (60 cm) high.
Flowers: the petals green or greenish, the hoods (the upper part of the flower) violet to purple.
Leaves: alternate, on very short stalks, broad oblong, narrowing toward base, to 4½" (12 cm) long.

viridis, Latin, "green."

Asclepias verticillata Whorled Milkweed
May–Sept.

Habitat: upland fields, prairies, glades, wasteland, edges of woods. Plant to 2½ feet (76 cm) tall.
Flowers: small umbels arising from the upper leaf nodes, white to greenish.
Leaves: in many whorls with a few leaves per whorl, linear, to 2" (5 cm) long, threadlike.

verticillata, Latin, "whorled."

Asclepias hirtella Florida Milkweed
May–Aug.

Habitat: prairies and glades, absent from Ozarks and Southeast Lowlands, to 3 feet (90 cm) tall.
Flowers: stalked umbels arising from the upper leaf axils, greenish petals with white margins, quite small. Stems and flower stalks hairy.
Leaves: narrow, lance-shaped with prominent side veins on underside.

hirtella, Latin, "somewhat hairy."

Asclepias viridiflora Green Milkweed
May–Aug.

Habitat: glades, prairies; statewide except some northern counties, to 3 feet (90 cm) tall.
Flowers: lack a horn in the cavity of the hood, light to dark green in fairly large, tight umbels arising from upper leaf axils.
Leaves: variable in shape; linear, lanceolate, oval or intermediate shapes; opposite, on short petioles, to 5" (13 cm) long.

viridiflora, Latin, "green-flowered."

Asclepias incarnata Swamp Milkweed
June–Sept.

Habitat: moist bottomlands, especially in Missouri and Mississippi floodplains; statewide except Southeast Lowlands. On long, smooth, flexible stems, to 7 feet (more than 2 m) tall, often the dominant plant in bottomlands.
Flowers: in many loose umbels, mostly terminal; pink or quite rarely white with a delicate fragrance.
Leaves: mostly opposite, narrow lanceolate to 6" (15 cm) long.

incarnata, Latin, "in the flesh," the floral color.

Asclepias quadrifolia (92) Four-leaved Milkweed
May–June

Habitat: open woods, usually upland, absent from northwest one-third of state. Normally 12–15" (30–38 cm) tall but occasionally higher.
Flowers: loose umbels, either upright or drooping, from 1 to 3 umbels, white or pink, nicely fragrant.
Leaves: in 3 or 4 sets of which one of the upper sets has 4 leaves in a whorl, the others with 2 leaves. Shape broad lanceolate, pointed at both ends.

This is the only *Asclepias* species growing in woods in Missouri.

quadrifolia, Latin, "four-leaved."

Cynanchum laeve (52) Angle-Pod
July–Sept.

(Also known as *Ampelamus albidus* and *Gonolobus laevis*.)

Habitat: cultivated land, gardens, roadsides, thickets; statewide except south-central counties. Perennial, vigorous, aggressive climber which covers fences and shrubs.

Flowers: corolla lobes upright around a fleshy corona, white, tiny, in open groups arising on stalks from the leaf axils, strongly scented.

Leaves: heart-shaped to deltoid, opposite, to 3" (8 cm) long.

Fruit: a large, tapering pod; seeds are released on warm days in late winter or early spring. *C. laeve* has been recommended as food for bees, but has become a nuisance weed.

Cynanchum, Greek, "dog strangler"; *laeve*, Latin, "smooth."

Matelea decipiens (85) Climbing Milkweed
May–June

Habitat: rocky open woods, along streams, Ozarks north to Missouri River. A climbing or trailing vine.

Flowers: spreading corolla lobes, like a 5-pointed star, brown; the flower clusters arise on stalks from the opposite leaf axils.

Leaves: broadly ovate, heart-shaped, 5" (13–15 cm) long.

The species is one of 4 very similar ones in Missouri.

Matelea is the name of a vine growing on Martinique which for some unknown reason was given to these climbing milkweeds; *decipiens*, Latin, "deceiving," possibly because the floral structure differs so much from the characteristics of the Milkweed Family.

Composite Family *Asteraceae* (Compositae)

One of the largest plant families, with about 1,000 genera and 20,000 species worldwide. See page 16 for botanical details. A few genera cannot be fitted into a generalized description (ragweed, cocklebur, burdock). Foodplants: lettuce, salsify, Jerusalem artichoke, sunflower, grown for oil as is niger (*Guizotia abyssinica*) of Africa and India, used in U.S. as birdfood. Garden plants: aster, stokesia, ageratum, gaillardia, dahlia, calendula, cosmos, coreopsis and many more. Largest family in Missouri, with 78 genera and 274 species.

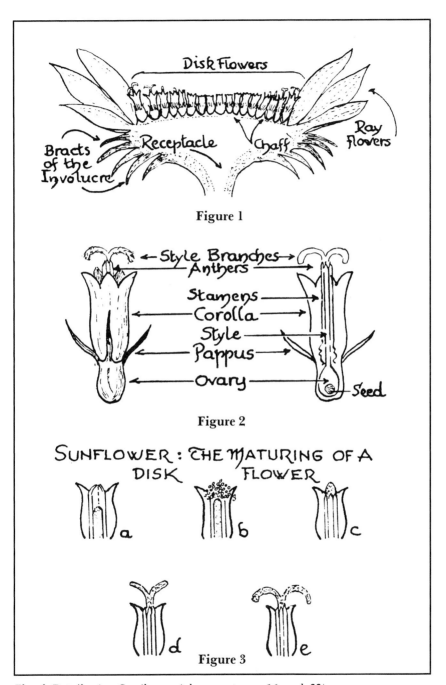

Figure 1

Figure 2

SUNFLOWER: THE MATURING OF A DISK FLOWER

Figure 3

Floral Detail of a Sunflower (also see pages 16 and 22)

Asteraceae (Ray Flowers Only)

Figure 1 Cross-section of a sunflower-type flowerhead. Ray flowers (or florets) either neutral (without "sexual" parts) or pistillate (female parts only), the latter may be either fertile or not, depending on genus and species. No sepals. Florets separated by "chaff," papery scales or bracts. All florets—disk and ray—inserted on a receptacle, which in turn is enclosed in bracts called "involucre." Florets open over a long period from the rim inward.

Figure 2 Side-view and cross-section of a "perfect" floret (having functional male and female parts). The 1-seeded ovary topped by scales or hair, the "pappus."

Figure 3 Avoiding self-fertilization. a) Five immature stamens, joined around style, but not connected to it, keep growing upward as is the pistil. b) Mature anthers shed large amounts of pollen, nearly filling floral cup. c) Short-lived pollen has been removed, usually by insects; style pushes through anthers. d) Style branches start to open. e) when fully open they accept pollen from another floret, i.e. they are receptive.

ASTERACEAE *(Ray Flowers Only)*

Cichorium intybus (115) Chicory, Blue Sailors
May–Oct.

Habitat: fields, pastures, waste areas, roadsides; statewide except Southeast Lowlands. Native of Old World. Shrublike with stiff, angular branches, to 3 feet (90 cm) tall. Will flower inches above ground after being mowed down. A common roadside weed.

Flowerheads: emerge all along stems with light blue or white ray florets, strap-shaped, toothed at end.

Leaves: resemble dandelion with prominent center vein, deep lobes and often spines. Upper branch leaves may be entire, without stems and narrow.

Root: used as adulterant or flavoring for coffee.

Cichorium, adaptation of an Arabian word for coffee, as is chicory; *intybus*, the Latin name of the plant.

Hieracium gronovii (68) Hawkweed
May–Oct.

Habitat: rocky, dry, open woods, fields, ravines in eastern, central and southern counties. Variable in size from 12" to over 2½ feet (30–75 cm), very hairy.

Flowerheads: few to many, terminal, each with a peduncle (stem), in open clusters, yellow, small, about ½" (8 mm) across.

Leaves: the basal broadly obovate, very hairy, variable in length to 8" (20 cm). Stem leaves smaller, becoming sessile, also very hairy.

Hieracium, Greek, name of a plant named for a hawk; *gronovii* for Jan Henry Gronovius, 1794–1830.

Krigia biflora (64) Dwarf Dandelion
May–Aug.

Habitat: open woods, near streams, in fields and meadows, generally south of the Missouri River. To 2 feet (60 cm) tall.

Flowerhead: dandelionlike but somewhat smaller, orange-yellow, to 1½" (4 cm) across, terminal on stems which normally have one clasping leaf midway on the stalk. The botanical name "biflora," (with 2 flowers) is misleading, as the plant may have any number of flowerheads.

Leaves: the basal on a long peduncle, spoonlike. Stem leaves one to few, much reduced, clasping.

Krigia named for the German physician David Krieg who collected plants in Maryland in the 18th century; *biflora*, see text above.

Krigia dandelion Potato Dandelion
April–June

Habitat: acid soils of prairies, glades, roadsides south of the Missouri River. Flowerstalk near 12" (30 cm) tall.

Flowerhead: dandelionlike, one only, terminal on a stalk, bright yellow. The stalk is neither hollow nor contains a milky juice, characteristic of the true dandelion.

Leaves: basal only to 6" (15 cm) long with a few lobes and teeth, reminiscent of dandelion.

Root: bears potatolike tubers.

dandelion, French, "dent de lion," lion-tooth.

Krigia virginica Dwarf Dandelion
April–Aug.

Habitat: usually in acid soils, crevices of sandstone and igneous outcroppings, prairies, meadows south of Missouri River and east-central counties. Truly a miniature dandelion, seldom over 3" (7½ cm) high.

Flowerhead: terminal, only one on each scape (a leafless flower stalk).

Leaves: basal, narrow, lobed and toothed, to 5" (12½ cm) long.

Plant forms large colonies, often lining the cracks in rocks.

Lactuca floridana (117) False Lettuce
Aug.–Oct.

Habitat: waste areas, wooded slopes, open woods, near streams, roadsides, railroads; statewide. One of 7 lettuce species of Missouri, to 8 feet (2.4 m) tall.

Asteraceae (Ray Flowers Only)

Flowerheads: open panicles with up to 17 florets in one head. Rayflowers light blue to nearly white, open a few at a time.

Leaves: mostly on stems, to 12" (30 cm) long, deeply lobed almost to midrib, toothed.

All parts of plant contain a milky juice. This is a true lettuce and is edible in salads or as "greens."

Lactuca, Latin, "milk."

Lactuca scariola Prickly Lettuce
June–Oct.

Habitat: waste areas, fields, roadsides; statewide. A tall weed from Europe, often 7 feet (2.1 m) high or more, believed to be an ancestor of the garden lettuce.

Flowerheads: in open inflorescences on long stalks, small, with light yellow strap-flowers, turning light blue on wilting.

Leaves: either without lobes or deep cuts or deeply lobed and cut, both types with prickly teeth on margins and the mid-rib of underside of leaf, clasping, thin, from 2-12" (5-30 cm) long.

scariola, from Latin *scariosus*, thin, membranous (the stem leaves).

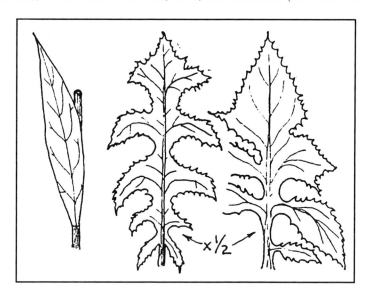

Lactuca leaves, from left, *canadensis, scariola, floridana*

Lactuca canadensis Wild Lettuce
July–Sept.

Habitat: borders of woods, fields, mud banks, gravel bars; statewide.

Very similar to *L. scariola* but LEAVES do NOT clasp the stems and are either entire without prickles or deeply lobed with prickles.

Pyrrhopappus carolinianus (64) False Dandelion
May–Oct.

Habitat: fields, dry or wet areas, roadsides, waste places; statewide. Depending on soil and moisture, from 12" to 3 feet (30–90 cm) tall. Exists either as an annual or winter annual, when leaves are produced in 1 year and the flowers in the next.
Flowerheads: like dandelion but sulphur yellow, several or only one, terminal.
Leaves: the basal either entire or pinnatifid (like dandelion leaves), have often disappeared by flowering time. The stem leaves, if present, can be quite large—to 6" (15 cm) long; few, either lanceolate, oblong, entire or pinnatifid; toothed, partly clasping, sessile.

Pyrrhopappus Greek, *"pyr"* fire, and *"pappos"* down, the bristles or hair of the seed covers (achenes), which are rusty to brick-red.

Tragopogon dubius (62) Goat's Beard
May–July

Habitat: fields, meadows, waste areas, roadsides, railroads; statewide. Native of Europe. Fleshy stalks, single or several to 2½ feet (76 cm).
Flowerheads: surrounded by narrow bracts which are longer than the yellow ray florets. Stems considerably thickened just below flowerheads, which are large and showy but closed by noon on sunny days.
Leaves: narrow linear, both basal and caudal, the latter clasping and alternate.
Fruit: seedheads handsome and large, much like those of dandelion.

Tragopogon, Greek, "goat's beard," *dubius*, Latin, "doubtful," because the plant was long mistaken for another species.

Tragopogon porrifolius Salsify or Oyster Plant
May–July

Habitat: waste places, roadsides; scattered along roads in central Missouri. Very similar to *T. dubius* but flowerheads are purple with slightly broader leaves. Were it not for mowing, *T. porrifolius* would spread along roads and highways. Introduced from Europe.

porrifolius, Latin, "with the leaf of a leek."

ASTERACEAE (*Disk Flowers Only*)

Antennaria plantaginifolia (28) Pussy's Toes, Everlasting,
April–June Indian Tobacco

Habitat: dry, rocky, often wooded slopes on acid soils; statewide. Densely
hairy plant with flower stems to 10" (25 cm) tall.
Flowerheads: either "male" or "female" in tight clusters (dioecious).
Styles of female florets often crimson. Inflorescense white to off-
white.
Leaves: both basal and caudal (on the stems). The basal leaves paddle-
shaped on long stems with 3 prominent ribs, appear usually after
flowering has started. Caudal leaves few, almost linear, short.

The plant is an indicator of acid soil. The fuzzy flowerheads
account for the name "Pussy's Toes."

Antennaria, Latin, "with antenna," referring to the styles of the
female inflorescenses; *plantaginifolia*, Latin, "with leaves of a plantain."

Antennaria neglecta Field Cat's-Foot or Pussy's Toes
April–June

Habitat: fields, prairies, open woods in north, west and central Missouri.
Very much like *A. plantaginifolia* but LEAVES are much smaller
and have only one central nerve.

neglecta, Latin, "neglected" or "overlooked."

Cacalia atriplicifolia (49) Pale Indian Plantain
June–Oct.

Habitat: low and upland woods, roadsides, railroads; statewide. Single
stem with a silvery coating, to 5 feet (1.5 m) tall, with widely
spaced leaves and terminal, spreading inflorescense. Likes shade.
Flowerheads: a flat-topped, loose corymb. Whitish disk florets surrounded by long, stiff green bracts.
Leaves: pale green above, silvery-white (glaucous) below, stand out
obliquely, irregularly-shaped with pointed lobes, the lower ones
wider than long, to 6" (15 cm) wide.

Cacalia, ancient name of uncertain meaning; *atriplicifolia*, Latin,
"with a leaf of *Atriplex*," the saltbush.

Cacalia muhlenbergii Great Indian Plantain
May–Sept.

Habitat: rich woods of north or east-facing slopes, not found in western third of state. Very similar to *C. atriplicifolia* but LEAVES are green on both sides, the lower ones kidney-shaped, often wider than long with many long teeth.

muhlenbergii for Gottfried Heinrich Ernst Muhlenberg, 1753–1815, the plant's discoverer.

Cacalia tuberosa Indian Plantain
May–Aug.

Habitat: glades and prairies, absent from northern and Southeast Lowland counties. Stalks to 3 feet (90 cm) tall, entirely different in appearance from the other members of the genus.
Flowerheads: open panicles, terminal, flat-topped as in an umbel, white with greenish bracts.
Leaves: on conspicuously long stems, elliptical, tapering to base with parallel veins. Stem leaves few, much smaller, all leaves entire.

tuberosa, Latin, with a tuberous root.

Carduus nutans (100) Musk Thistle, Nodding Thistle
June–Oct.

Habitat: waste places, roadsides, railroads; spreading statewide. To 6 feet (1.8 m) tall. Native of Europe.
Flowerheads: to 2½" (7 cm) across, rose-purple, supported by pointed, recurved bracts. Mature heads nod.
Leaves: two kinds: a basal rosette, leaves very long, deeply lobed and spiny, to 10" (25 cm) long, with a prominent, nearly white midrib. The basal rosette is developed during the first year, stays green all winter, killing all plants it covers. The upright stalk grows during the second year with smaller, very spiny leaves.
Seeds: up to 10,000 produced by one plant, spread by silky parachutes.

The species came to the U.S. early in the 20th century and is spreading rapidly.

Carduus, Latin, the classical Roman name for thistle; *nutans,* Latin, "nodding."

Asteraceaee (Disk Flowers Only)

Centaurea cyanus (114) Cornflower
May–Sept.

Habitat: fields, waste places, roadsides; scattered statewide. Native of Europe, much-branched, to 3 feet (90 cm) tall; annual garden plant, often escaped. It may cover entire fields.

Flowerheads: about 1" (2½ cm) across with a vase-shaped involucre (the bracts), in "cornflower" blue, pink or whitish.

Leaves: narrow, linear, sharply pointed, alternate.

Cornflower's name comes from the German *Kornblume*. *Korn* in German means wheat, oats or barley, and *C. cyanus* is a common weed in grain fields. The name has nothing to do with the American "corn" (*zea mays*). **Centaurea** named after the centaur Chiron, a healer; *cyanus*, Greek, "blue."

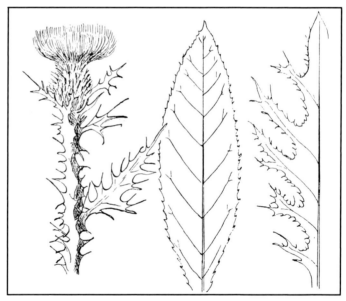

Cirsium leaves, from left, *vulgare, altissimum, discolor*

Cirsium vulgare (100) Bull Thistle
June–Sept.

Habitat: fields, waste places, roadsides; statewide. Native of Europe, to 7 feet (2.1 m) tall, the upper stems and branches winged with a wavy, prickly tissue.

Flowerheads: typical thistles, pale lavender or rose lavender with a prominent involucre (the floral bracts), which are covered with a fine, cobweblike silk.

Leaves: deeply lobed, hairy, spiny, the upper surface with stiff bristles. This thistle, like all others, is a favorite of goldfinches. An identification mark is the spines growing right up to the flowerheads.

Cirsium, Latin, "swelled vein," a problem for which thistles were supposed to be a remedy; *vulgare*, Latin, "common."

Cirsium altissimum Tall Thistle
July–Oct.

Habitat: slopes or bottomland, roadsides; statewide. To 10 feet (3 m) tall, a native thistle.
Flowerheads: many, rose-purple or magenta, rarely white. Outer involucre bracts with a dark spot; all bracts end in a weak prickle.
Leaves: entire (not lobed) with marginal prickles only (none on the leaf surface), woolly, hairy underneath. Upper stem leaves narrow lanceolate with longer spines.

altissimum, Latin, "very tall" or "the tallest."

Cirsium discolor Field Thistle
Aug.–Nov.

Habitat: old fields, pastures, waste places, roadsides; probably statewide, having spread much in the last 25 years; the most often seen thistle in east-central Missouri, to 7 feet (2 m) tall.
Flowerheads: as in *C. altissimum*, usually pink-purple, sometimes white.
Leaves: long, deeply lobed with long-spined points. Leaf margins more or less turned under or downward with a continuous display of small spines.

discolor, Latin, "of two colors" (see above).

Elephantopus carolinianus (53) Elephant Foot
Aug.–Oct.

Habitat: wooded valleys, lowlands, openings in woods, south of Missouri River. A much-forked, shrublike plant to 3 feet (90 cm) tall.
Flowerheads: small clusters with only 2–5 florets (a glomerule), subtended by a few leaflike bracts which are longer than the glomerules. The light lavender to whitish flowers are bunched in a flat cluster. This makes the genus an unusual member of the Composite Family.
Leaves: scattered along stems, alternate, oval, obliquely toothed, the lower ones narrowed rather abruptly at the base, the upper ones normally sessile and quite small.

Elephantopus, Greek, "elephant foot," probably because some foreign members of the genus have large, elephant-foot-like leaves.

Asteraceae (Disk Flowers Only)

Eupatorium Key

1a Flowerheads gray or off-white

    2a) Leaves with long petioles, large teeth, *ovate to lanceolate.* Stems pulverulent (as covered with dust) . . . . *serotinum*

    2b) Leaves strongly 3-nerved, very short petioles or sessile, *slender lanceolate. Teeth above middle of leaves only* . . . . *altissimum*

    2c) Leaves sessile, lanceolate, to broadly lanceolate, rounded at base, *with teeth over entire margin* . . . . *sessilifolium*

    2d) Leaves perfoliate (opposite leaves united around the stem) . . . . *perfoliatum*

1b) Flowerheads *clear white.* Leaves with long petioles, large teeth, *broadly ovate; stems smooth* . . . . *rugosum*

1c) Flowerheads pale pink or pale purple. Leaves in whorls . . . . *purpureum*

1d) Flowerheads bright blue or violet . . . . *coelestinum*

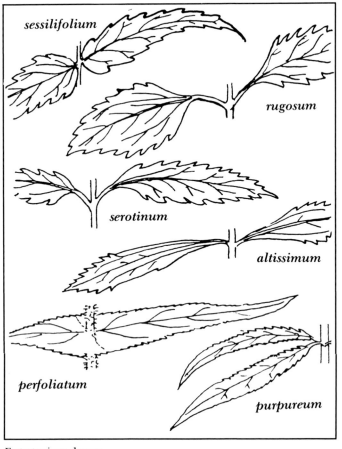

Eupatorium leaves

Eupatorium rugosum (51) White Snakeroot
July–Oct.

Habitat: rich or rocky woods, base of bluffs, clearings, roadsides, waste places; statewide. Upright, much-branched perennial to 4 feet (1.2 m) tall. Smooth stems.

Flowerheads: in loose, terminal, flat-topped clusters. Flowers point upward, clear white (*E. serotinum* is gray), tuftlike. Bracts of involucre acutely pointed, hairless.

Leaves: opposite, with long petioles, large teeth, broadly ovate.

This plant is the cause of "milk-sickness;" it is poisonous to cattle and killed many early settlers who drank poisoned milk, including Abraham Lincoln's mother.

Eupatorium named after an ancient Greek healer, Eupater ("good father") Mithridates; *rugosum,* Latin, "wrinkled," possibly referring to the leaves.

Eupatorium serotinum Late Boneset
Aug.–Oct.

Habitat: fields, waste places, roadsides, near moisture; statewide. Much branched perennial 3–4½ feet (3–4.5 dm) tall. Stems pulverulent (as covered with dust).

Flowerheads: very similar to rugosum but inflorescence spreads more and is distinctly gray with fewer florets (to 15). Bracts broadly rounded, densely hairy.

Leaves: long petioles, large teeth, ovate to lanceolate.

serotinum, Latin, "late" (flowering).

Eupatorium altissimum (53) Tall Thoroughwort
Aug.–Oct.

Habitat: prairies, fields, open woods, waste places; statewide but uncommon in Southeast Lowlands. Stout perennial to over 6 feet (2 m) tall.

Flowerheads: loose inflorescences with only 5 florets in each head, dull white. Bracts broad and rounded.

Leaves: opposite, strongly 3-nerved, very short petioles or sessile, slender lanceolate. Teeth above middle of leaves only.

altissimum, Latin, "very tall" or "tallest."

Eupatorium sessilifolium Upland Boneset
July–Sept.

Habitat: dry, rocky bluffs, along streams, scattered; statewide except in western counties. Perennial, to 6 feet (1.8 m) tall.

Asteraceae (Disk Flowers Only)

Flowerheads: open clusters with only 5 or 6 florets in a head and rounded bracts, dull white.
Leaves: opposite, without petioles, lanceolate with broadly rounded base with small teeth.

sessilifolium, Latin, "with stemless leaves."

Eupatorium perfoliatum Boneset
July–Oct.

Habitat: in moist situations; statewide. Hairy-stemmed perennial, to 6 feet (2 m) tall.
Flowerheads: flat-topped clusters with 9–23 florets in a head, dull white.
Leaves: to 8" (20 cm) long, triangular, with fine teeth, perfoliate (opposite leaves united around the stem).

perfoliatum, Latin, "going through the stem—the leaves, of course.

Eupatorium pupureum Green-stemmed Joe-Pye-weed
July–Sept.

Habitat: slopes and primarily low, wet bottomland; statewide. To 6 feet tall (2 m). The botanical name is misleading as the purple color shows only in the nodes.
Flowerheads: in large, domed clusters, very pale pink, purplish or off-white, 4–7 florets per head.
Leaves: whorls, lanceolate, pointed at both ends, to 12" (30 cm) long, toothed.
Stems: green with purplish streaking at leaf whorls.

purpureum, Latin, "purple."

Eupatorium coelestinum (117) Mist Flower, Wild Ageratum,
July–Oct.   Blue Boneset

Habitat: ditches, along lakes, streams or any low, moist area south of Missouri River. Often in large stands, normally 12–18" (30–45 cm) high.
Flowerheads: dense clusters, terminal or from leaf axils, blue or violet with from 35–70 florets per head.
Leaves: opposite on short stems, ovate to triangular with large teeth.

E. coelestinum resembles the annual *Ageratum* of the gardens. Under cultivation it spreads rapidly with an interwoven mass of roots and is highly aggressive.

coelestinum, Latin, "sky-blue." A white form exists but is rare in Missouri.

Asteraceae (Disk Flowers Only)

Liatris: Perennials with 9 species in Missouri, but only 4 have wide distribution. Flowers on upright spikes, pink/purple with overlapping (imbricate) bracts. The shape of the bracts determines the species.

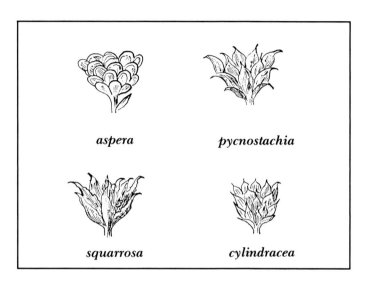

aspera   *pycnostachia*

squarrosa   *cylindracea*

Liatris bracts

Liatris aspera (104) Blazing Star, Gay Feather
Aug.-Nov.

Habitat: dry upland prairies, glades, roadsides, railroads; statewide except Southeast Lowlands. Unbranched stalks, 2 to 3 feet (60-90 cm) tall but higher under favorable conditions.
Flowerheads: many, uniform along a spikelike upper stalk, rose-purple. Bracts rounded, somewhat spreading. Heads have 16-35 florets.
Leaves: alternate, the lowest to 15" (38 cm) long with a petiole, the upper ones much shorter becoming sessile, narrow lance-shaped.
Root: a round corm.

Liatris, a name of unknown meaning; *aspera,* Latin, "rough."

Liatris pycnostachya (104) Blazing Star, Gay Feather, Button
July-Oct.   Snakeroot

Habitat: prairies, open ground, along roads and railroads; statewide except Southeast Lowlands. Unbranched stalks, to 5 feet (1.5 m) tall, sometimes seen by the thousands, hairy throughout.
Flowerheads: densely crowded around upper spikelike stalk, rose-purple. Bracts recurved with sharp points.

Asteraceae (Disk Flowers Only)

Leaves: quite narrow, the lower to 20" (50 cm) long, becoming much shorter higher up.
Root: a rounded corm.

pycnostachya, Greek, "thick-spiked," possibly referring to the leaves or the flowerheads.

Liatris squarrosa Scaly Blazing Star
June–Sept.

Habitat: rocky glades, bluffs, open woods, absent from northwest and Southeast Lowlands. A much lower *Liatris* than the above, to about 2½ feet (75 cm) tall.
Flowerheads: few, spaced apart, with 20–45 florets per head and up to 60 in the terminal head, rose-purple. Bracts long-pointed and spreading.
Leaves: linear to a little broader.

squarrosa, Latin, "spreading" (the bracts).

Liatris cylindracea Cylindric Blazing Star
July–Sept.

Habitat: glades, bluffs; south and east-central Missouri. To 2 feet (6 dm) tall.
Flowerheads: few, on stiff, short stems (peduncles), with 10–35 florets, rose-purple. Bracts rounded with short tips, the involucre in a vase shape.
Leaves: linear or nearly so, to 10" (25 cm) long.

cylindracea, Latin, "in a cylinder" (the bracts).

Vernonia Key

1a) Mainly growing in dry areas.
    2a) bracts broad and long-pointed . . . . *baldwinii*
1b) Mainly growing in moist bottomland or on gravel bars
    2b) bracts slender, long-tapering, pointed, spreading . . . . . . *crinata*
    2c) bracts rounded without a tip, from 13–30 florets in a head . . . . *altissima*
    2d) bracts tightly packed (appressed) purple or green midvein, either rounded or pointed, 34–60 florets in a head . . . . . . *missurica*
    2e) bracts rounded, a few coming to a point, finely hairy
    . . . . *fasciculata*

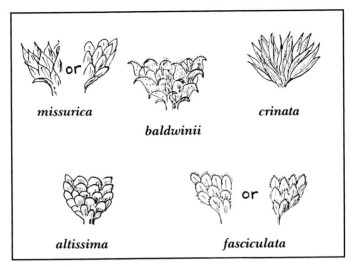

missurica

baldwinii

crinata

altissima

fasciculata

Vernonia bracts

Vernonia baldwinii (96) Ironweed
May–Sept.

Habitat: fields, glades, along roads and railroads; statewide. To 4 feet
(1.2 m) tall.

Flowerheads: very numerous, rose-purple with many florets (to 34) in
a head. Bracts broad and long-pointed. This is the earliest flowering
of the 5 Missouri *Vernonia* species.

Leaves: alternate, hairy, lanceolate, sharply pointed at both ends with
short stems and fine teeth, to about 6" (15 cm) long.

Vernonia, named for William Vernon, a 17th century botanist and
explorer who collected in Maryland in 1698; *baldwinii* for William
Baldwin, 1779-1819, the original collector of the plant.

Vernonia crinita Great Ironweed
July–Sept.

Habitat: gravel and sandbars south of the Missouri River. To 4 feet
(1.2 m) tall, sometimes in large, spectacular clumps.

Flowerheads: irregular inflorescences, heads with 55–89 florets, bright
rose-purple. Bracts slender, long-tapering, pointed, spreading.

Leaves: linear to lanceolate with a few small teeth or none.

crinita, Latin, "long hairy," which the plant is NOT.

Vernonia missurica Ironweed
July–Sept.

Habitat: moist prairies, meadows, streamsides, low wooded land; statewide except western Ozarks. To 4 feet (1.2 m) tall.

Asteraceae (Disk Flowers Only) and (Disk and Ray Flowers)

Flowerheads: look like *V. baldwinii* with exception of the bracts which are tightly packed, purple or green midvein, either rounded or pointed.

Leaves: similar to *V. crinita*, but thinly to thickly hairy with long hair.

Vernonia altissima Tall Ironweed
July–Sept.

Habitat: moist places in low woods, along streams, alluvial ground, scattered mainly in eastern and central Missouri. Also to 4 feet (1.2 m) tall but at times much taller.

Flowerheads: numerous, 13–30 florets in a head, rose-purple. Bracts rounded without a tip.

Leaves: lanceolate, to 10" (25 cm) long, serrate to nearly entire.

altissima, Latin, "very tall" or "tallest."

Vernonia fasciculata Western Ironweed
July–Sept.

Habitat: wet situations in lowlands, absent from most of Ozark region. To 4 feet (1.2 m) tall.

Flowerheads: densely flowered, usually flat inflorescences, with 18–21 florets in a head. Rose-purple. Bracts rounded, a few coming to a point, finely hairy.

Leaves: lanceolate, pointed at both ends with small to larger teeth. Underside pitted with dotlike depressions.

fasciculata, Latin, "clustered" or "in bundles," refers to the flowerheads.

ASTERACEAE *(Disk and Ray Flowers)*

Achillea millefolium (45) Yarrow, Milfoil
May–Nov.

Habitat: fields, roadsides, waste places; statewide. Frequently the dominant (invasive) plant. Native of Europe. Simple or branched stem, to 2½ feet (70 cm) tall.

Flowerheads: in dense, flat-topped clusters, terminal. Ray florets minute, white, rarely light pink, disk light yellow.

Leaves: finely dissected, fernlike, to 10" (25 cm) long, narrow oblong. Yarrow has a strong, pungent odor and serves in Europe as sheep fodder (*Schafgarbe*).

Achillea, Greek for Achilles, a hero who is supposed to have used the plant to treat wounds; *millefolium*, Latin, "thousand leaves"; milfoil, French, "thousand leaves."

Aster: There are 29 species found in Missouri, of which 20 are widely distributed. Three species have been selected as typical.

Aster novae-angliae (105) New England Aster
Aug.-Oct.

Habitat: moist prairies, meadows, roadsides, streams; statewide except Southeast Lowlands. Tallest of our asters, to 8 feet (2.4 m) tall, branching toward top of stems.

Flowerheads: many, about the size of a quarter, with many ray florets; variable in color: crimson, magenta, shades of purple, lavender. The disk yellow.

Leaves: many, alternate, narrow lanceolate, clasping the stem and auriculate (with ears). Selections of this species are much used in gardens.

> *Aster,* Latin, "star" (the flowers); *novae angliae,* Latin, "of New England."

Aster oblongifolius (118) Oblong-Leaf Aster
July-Nov.

Habitat: glades and open, rocky slopes; south of Missouri River and eastern counties north of it; absent from southeastern counties. Perennials, rarely to 3 feet (1 m) tall, branched.

Flowerheads: terminal, few to many, with 20-40 ray florets; blue or purple, rarely rose.

Leaves: sessile, narrow, clasping the stem, with or without small "ears," oblong to lance-shape, from 1-3½" (2-9 cm) long.

> *oblongifolius,* Latin, "oblong-leaved."

Aster pilosus (51) White Heath Aster
Aug.-Nov.

Habitat: old fields, gravel bars, waste places; statewide. Much-branched, to 5 feet (1.5 m) tall, with branches spreading or ascending, hairy or not.

Flowerheads: each on its own peduncle (stem), which usually has a number of tiny bracts; 16-35 white ray florets with a yellow disk about 3/4" (20 mm) across.

Leaves: linear, usually less than 3/8" (1 cm) wide, variable in length.

> *pilosus,* Latin, "with soft hair."

Asteraceae (Disk and Ray Flowers)

Bidens: Of 10 species reported for Missouri, only 1 has a wide distribution. Most species demand moist or wet habitats.

Bidens polylepis (78) Beggar Ticks, Tickseed Sunflower
Aug.-Oct.

Habitat: wet situations of prairies, waste places, ditches, roadsides, railroads; statewide. Much-branched, to 7 feet (2.1 m) tall. Often in massive displays in moist bottomlands.
Flowerheads: daisylike, bright yellow, with usually 8 ray florets, heads about 1 1/4" (3 cm) across. Ray florets pointed. Bracts long, pointed, in 2 unequal rows.
Leaves: pinnate (like a feather) with 3 to 5 divisions, pointed, each with large teeth.
Fruit: seeds ticklike with 2 needlelike awns which attach themselves to man and beast, thus "tickseed" and "beggar-tick."

Bidens, Latin, "two teeth"; *polylepis,* Greek, "with many scales," possibly referring to the bracts.

Chrysanthemum leucanthemum (45) Ox-eye Daisy
May-Aug.

Habitat: fields, meadows, roadsides; statewide. Stems to 3 feet (90 cm) tall with few branches. Native of Eurasia; provides spectacular displays in summer.
Flowerheads: large, to 2" (5 cm) across with white ray florets and a yellow disk.
Leaves: the basal on petioles, spoon-shaped, lobed, the upper leaves sessile with blunt lobes, toothlike.

Chrysanthemum, Greek, "golden flower," refers to the European type species *C. coronarium* with yellow flowers; *leucanthemum,* Greek, "white flower," the combined genus and species name seems a contradiction—"the golden white flower."

Chrysopsis villosa (74) Golden Aster
June-Oct.

Habitat: prairies, fields, roadsides, railroads south of Missouri River. Much-branched, to 3 feet (90 cm) tall, 1 of 2 plants called "golden aster" in Missouri. Neither is botanically an aster. At times covers entire valleys.
Flowerheads: bright yellow, to 1½" (4 cm) across, bracts purple-tipped.
Leaves: hairy (as are the stems), alternate, sessile with a few small teeth, to 3" (7.5 cm) long, elliptical and pointed.

Chrysopsis, Greek, "golden eye"; *villosa,* Latin, "soft hairy."

Asteraceae (Disk and Ray Flowers)

Coreopsis Of 6 species recorded in Missouri, 2 are not common.

Coreopsis Key

1a) Leaves undivided and mostly basal . . . . *lanceolata*
1b) Leaves divided, but NOT to their base, sessile . . . . *palmata*
1c) Leaves divided into usually 3 leaflets with stems
    2a) leaflets fairly even in size . . . . *tripteris*
    2b) center leaflet much longer than lateral leaflets . . . *pubescens*

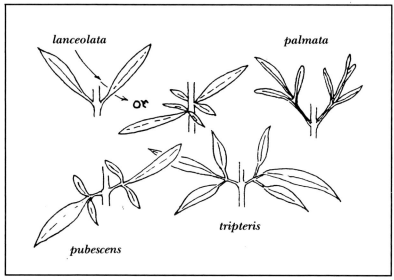

Coreopsis leaves

Coreopsis lanceolata (60) Tickseed Coreopsis
April–June

Habitat: prairies, glades, roadsides, railroads, Ozark region north to Missouri River. Usually several stems, to 2 feet (6 dm) tall, a prominent glade species.

Flowerheads: few, with large heads, about 2" (5 cm) across, the ray florets typically broad, yellow, the ends sharply toothed.

Leaves: narrow, undivided, mostly at lower part of stems.

When grown in gardens ***Coreopsis*** demands excellent drainage and full sun, but seems to prefer poor soil.

Coreopsis, Greek, "resembling a bug" (the seeds); ***lanceolata,*** Latin, "lance-shaped."

Asteraceae (Disk and Ray Flowers)

Coreopsis palmata Stiff Tickseed
May–July

Habitat: prairies, fallow fields, roadsides; statewide. Rigid perennial to 3 feet (90 cm) tall.
Flowerheads: few, on short peduncles, yellow, the ray florets toothed.
Leaves: deeply 3-lobed, the lobes linear-oblong, like the footprint of a large shorebird.

palmata, Latin, "like a hand" (the leaves).

Coreopsis tripteris (74) Tall Tickseed
July–Sept.

Habitat: prairies, open woods, roadsides; statewide except Southeast Lowlands. Tall, late-blooming, well-branched, to 8 feet (2.4 m) tall.
Flowerheads: open, terminal inflorescences, to 1½" (4 cm) across, yellow, 6–10 ray florets, with an anise scent.
Leaves: on stems, deeply 3–5 divided nearly to base, segments lance-shaped without teeth.

tripteris, tri-, Latin, "three," *-pteris,* Greek, "wing," the leaves.

Coreopsis pubescens Star Tickseed
May–Sept.

Habitat: moist situations, valleys, woods, gravel bars, in Ozark region, 2–4 feet (6 dm–1.2 m) tall, all green parts with loosely spreading hair, usually not much-branched.
Flowerheads: terminal, yellow, the ray florets with typical teeth at end margin.
Leaves: lower on short petioles, oval; stem-leaves relatively broad on short petioles, the highest sessile, to 10" (25 cm) long. A few leaves with short side lobes.

pubescens, Latin, "downy hairy."

Echinacea pallida (93) Pale-purple Coneflower
May–July

Habitat: prairies, limestone glades, roadsides, railroads; statewide except Southeast Lowlands. Unbranched, to 3 feet (90 cm) tall, stems with spreading hair.
Flowerheads: ray florets slender straps, the ends notched, hanging down, rose or magenta, rarely white. Disk knoblike, brown with yellow stamens protruding.
Leaves: the basal on very long petioles, lanceolate, to 8" (20 cm) long; stem leaves much shorter and with shorter stems; both types densely hairy.

The plant is used for medicinal purposes and threatened by root diggers.

Echinacea, Greek, "hedgehog," a spiny mammal, referring to the bracts of the inflorescence; *pallida,* Latin, "pale."

Asteraceae (Disk and Ray Flowers)

Echinacea purpurea (99) Purple Coneflower
May–Oct.

Habitat: openings in moist woods, wooded bottomland, prairies, scattered in mid-, eastern and southern Missouri, showy, to 2½ feet (1.5 m) tall.

Flowerheads: usually solitary, terminal, quite large; the disk madder-purple, the long ray florets shades of magenta, from 10–20.

Leaves: the basal long petioled, to 6" (15 cm) long, coarsely toothed, oblong, rounded at base; upper leaves smaller, lanceolate with or without stems.

purpurea, Latin, "purple."

Erigeron Key

1a) Flowerheads ¾–1½" (2–4 cm) across
    2a) leaves spoon-shaped . . . . *pulchellus*
    2b) leaves elliptical, toothed . . . . *annuus*
    2c) leaves spade-shaped with ears . . . . *philadelphicus*
    2d) leaves narrow, lance-shaped . . . . *strigosus*
1b) Flowerheads small, to 3/16" (6 mm) across
    3a) tall, to 7 feet (2.1 m) . . . . *canadensis*
    3b) low, to 1 foot (30 cm) . . . . *divaricatus*

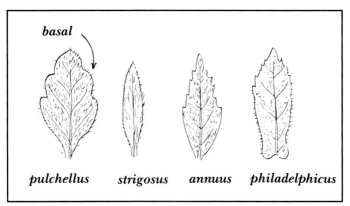

Erigeron leaves

Erigeron philadelphicus (31) Philadelphia Fleabane
April–June

Habitat: fields, valleys, waste places, roadsides, railroads; scattered throughout the state. Perennial, to 3 feet (90 cm) tall, branched toward top, commonly soft, hairy.

Flowerheads: small "daisies" with up to nearly 200 ray florets, white, turning light pink-lavender. No other *Erigeron* has so many ray florets.

Leaves: lower ones spade-shaped with lobes, obtuse tips, short stems, crenate. Upper leaves stemless, partially clasping, pointed oblong.

171

Asteraceae (Disk and Ray Flowers)

Erigeron pulchellus Robin's Plantain
April–June

Habitat: woods, clearings, along streams, roadsides; missing from northwest counties. To 2 feet (60 cm) tall but usually much lower.

Flowerheads: one to a few, larger than any other native *Erigeron*, to 1 3/8" (4 cm) across, white, often pinkish.

Leaves: very hairy, spoon-shaped near base of plant, narrower on stems.

pulchellus, Latin, "pretty."

Erigeron annuus Daisy Fleabane
May–Oct.

Habitat: fields, prairies, waste places; statewide. Leafy and hairy plant, to 1 yard (9 dm) tall.

Flowerheads: many, with 80–125 rays, white or pinkish.

Leaves: elliptical, coarsely toothed, to 4" (10 cm) long with long stems; stem leaves much shorter, numerous, most of them toothed. Leaves have conspicuously hairy margins.

annuus, Latin, "annual" or "yearly," the lifetime of the species.

Erigeron strigosus Daisy Fleabane
May–Sept.

Habitat: dry woods, glades, fields; statewide. Similar to *annuus* but smaller, usually to 2 feet (60 cm) tall, hairy.

Flowerheads: few to many, smaller than in *E. annuus*, about 3/4" (2½ cm) across. White with yellow center.

Leaves: the basal oblanceolate with few or no teeth, stem leaves few, linear, sessile, without teeth. All are hairy.

strigosus, Latin, "with spreading hair."

Erigeron canadensis Horse Weed
June–Nov.

Habitat: fields, roadsides, waste places; statewide. Very tall, commonly to 7 feet (2.1 m), entirely different in appearance from the other *Erigeron* species.

Flowerheads: many, in a dense, elongate, terminal inflorescence. Heads tiny, about 3/16" (5 mm) across, the rays so small that they are seen with a magnifying lens only.

Leaves: many, alternate around the single, hairy stem. They are also hairy.

Asteraceae (Disk and Ray Flowers)

Erigeron divaricatus Dwarf Fleabane
May–Sept.

Habitat: fields, prairies, waste places; statewide. Low, much-branched, hairy, to 1 foot (30 cm) high.
Flowerheads: numerous, terminal, minute.
Leaves: narrow linear, to 3/4" (4 cm) long. The species is an annual. Note the bushy, ash-gray appearance.

divaricatus, Latin, "spreading."

Helenium amarum (73) Sneezeweed, also Bitterweed,
June–Oct. Yellow Dog-Fennel

Habitat: fields, waste places, roadsides, railroads, in southern and west-central Missouri. Much-branched, usually to 12" (30 cm) high, but rarely to twice that.
Flowerheads: few to many on naked stems above the foliage, yellow, the 5–10 ray florets deflexed and notched; the disk bowl-shaped, pointing skyward, yellow.
Leaves: profuse, linear, to 1½" (4 cm) long with smaller leaves arising from axils of larger ones.

Plant contains a poisonous milk, thus also called bitterweed.

Helenium, named either for the Greek Helenus, son of Priam or Helena of Troy, the cause of the Trojan war; sneezeweed because the dried and powdered disk florets, used as a snuff, cause violent and prolonged sneezing; *amarum,* Latin, "bitter."

Helenium autumnale (78) Sneezeweed
Aug.–Nov.

Habitat: moist areas in meadows, prairies, ditches, along streams; state-wide except Southeast Lowlands. Late blooming, to 6 feet (1.8 cm) tall, stems conspicuously winged, branching toward top.
Flowerheads: many, all yellow with from 10–18 ray florets having notched ends and reflexed downward. The large disk is dome-shaped.
Leaves: alternate, narrow lanceolate, with or without a few teeth; the leaf tissue extending down the stem (decurrent).

All parts of plant contain a bitter substance which may be poison-ous.

autumnale, Latin, "of the fall."

Helenium flexuosum Purple-head Sneezeweed
June–Nov.

Habitat: moist places, bottomlands, ditches, roadsides, south of Missouri River and east-central counties. To 3 feet (90 cm) tall, branched toward top.

Asteraceae (Disk and Ray Flowers)

Flowerheads: few to many in an open inflorescence. The only **Helenium** with a deep brown-purple, domed disk and 10–15 reflexed yellow rays.

Leaves: lanceolate, sessile, to 5" (12 cm) long, the leaf tissue extending downward along the stems (decurrent).

flexuosum, Latin "turning" or "bending around," possibly referring to the recurved ray florets.

Helianthus: Of 16 species in Missouri, 10 have a limited distribution. All have yellow ray florets. "Sunflower," because the heads turn more or less with the sun from east to west each day. The ray flowers are neutral, having neither male nor female functional parts.

Helianthus Key

1a) Leaves with *long* petioles, petioles not winged
    2a) leaves large, ovate to broad, with irregular, large teeth, mostly alternate except uppermost . . . . *annuus*
1b) Leaves with winged petioles
    2b) leaves lance-shaped, coarsely toothed, long, prominently 3-veined, rough hairy above, downy below . . . . . . *tuberosus*
    2c) leaves long, coarsely toothed, lanceolate; petioles often with small wings; upper leaves closely spaced, usually alternate; lower leaves usually opposite . . . . *grosseserratus*
1c) Leaves sessile or with very short petioles
    2d) leaves densely gray-hairy, broadly ovate, opposite, teeth inconspicuous . . . . *mollis*
    2e) leaves fairly uniform, lanceolate, with very short petioles, almost all opposite, 9–15 below inflorescence; teeth small . *laetiflorus*
    2f) leaves variable, broadly lanceolate, rough hairy, *green* (not as in *mollis*), toothless, very short petioles . . . . *hirsutus*

Helianthus annuus (76) Common Sunflower
July–Nov.

Habitat: waste or cultivated land, roadsides, scattered; statewide. Extremely variable in height and appearance but easily to 7 feet (2.1 m) tall, with hairy stems.

Flowerheads: many, with brown disks, frequently a double set of ray florets, large.

Leaves: large, ovate to broad, with irregular, large teeth, mostly alternate except uppermost. Lower leaves on strong plants heart-shaped. All leaves rough, hairy.

Seeds: rich in oil and proteins, a mainstay of birds and small mammals.

This is the ancestor of the cultivated sunflower with huge flower-heads which was developed primarily in Russia; they revert eventually back to the wildflower size.

H. annuus is one of the few food staples contributed to the world by North America.

Helianthus, Greek, "sun-flower"; ***annuus***, Latin, "yearly," the life cycle of the species.

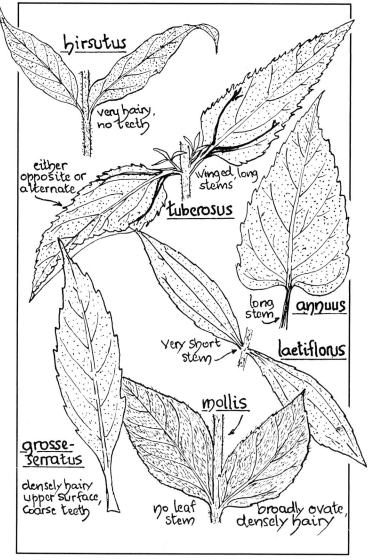

Helianthus leaves

175

Asteraceae (Disk and Ray Flowers)

Helianthus tuberosus (76) Jerusalem Artichoke
Aug.-Oct.

Habitat: moist areas of prairies, waste places, roadsides; absent from Ozarks. Very hairy, stalks 7–12 feet (2.1–3.6 m) tall, much-branched.

Flowerheads: sunflower-type with 12–20 ray florets, to 3" (8 cm) across, frequently with a distinct chocolate scent.

Leaves: with winged petioles, lance-shaped, coarsely toothed, long, prominently 3-veined, rough and hairy above, downy below, to 9" (23 cm) long.

Roots: potatolike, edible tubers, eaten by Indians and cultivated for human and animal food today. The tubers may be served to diabetics.

The name "Jerusalem artichoke" is probably based on a misunderstanding of the Italian name, *"girasol."*

tuberosus, Latin, "with tubers."

Helianthus grosseserratus (76) Sawtooth Sunflower
July-Oct.

Habitat: prairies, moist meadows and fields, roadsides, railroads; statewide except Southeast Lowlands. A giant to 16 feet (4.8 m) tall, usually branched; hybridizes readily (there are at least 11 known hybrid forms), making identification difficult.

Flowerheads: typical sunflower-type, all yellow, to 3½" (9 cm) across with 10–20 ray florets which are fairly wide.

Leaves: sessile or with very short petioles, long, coarsely toothed, lanceolate; petioles often with small wings; upper leaves closely spaced, usually alternate; lower leaves usually opposite, about 10" (25 cm) long and 2½" (6.5 cm) wide.

grosseserratus, Latin, "coarsely toothed."

Helianthus mollis Hairy or Ashy Sunflower
July-Oct.

Habitat: primarily prairies, also roadsides and fields, absent from northwest Missouri. To 4 feet (1.2 m) tall, usually much lower, spreading, very hairy.

Flowerheads: few, often a lemony yellow, to 3½" (9 cm) across.

Leaves: sessile, densely gray-hairy; broadly ovate, opposite, teeth inconspicuous.

mollis, Latin, "soft hairy."

Helianthus laetiflorus Prairie Sunflower
Aug.-Oct.

Habitat: prairies of northern and western Missouri. To 7 feet (2 m) tall, hairy.

Flowerheads: few, large, to 2½" (7 cm) across, usually with purple disks and 15-20 ray florets.
Leaves: fairly uniform, lanceolate, with very short petioles, almost all opposite, 9-15 below inflorescence; teeth small.

laetiflorus, Latin, "with a happy or pleasing flower."

Helianthus hirsutus Stiff-haired Sunflower
July-Oct.

Habitat: dry, open woods, prairies, roadsides; statewide. To 4 feet (1.2 m) tall with coarse, spreading hairs.
Flowerheads: all yellow with 8-15 ray florets, the rays often pointing upward.
Leaves: variable, broadly lanceolate, rough, hairy, green (as opposed to *mollis*), toothless, very short petioles; feel like sandpaper.

hirsutus, Latin, "hairy."

Heliopsis helianthoides (63) Oxeye, Sunflower Heliopsis,
May-Sept.   False Sunflower

Habitat: dry areas, edges of woods, roadsides, railroads, fields, waste places; statewide except Southeast Lowlands. Spreading, branched, sunflowerlike, of variable heighth 20"-5 feet (5 dm-1.5 m) tall.
Flowerheads: about 2" (5 cm) across, distinctly orange-yellow when young, fading to light yellow; rays 8-15, usually 10.
Leaves: opposite on long petioles, broadly ovate to nearly triangular, without hair; large, regular teeth.
Seeds: angular, while those of *Helianthus* species are flat.

Heliopsis, Greek, "sun-eye"; *helianthoides,* Greek, "like a sun-flower."

Parthenium integrifolium (41) American Feverfew,
May-Sept.   Wild Quinine

Habitat: prairies, glades, rocky open woods; statewide except Southeast Lowlands and northwest counties. Perennial, to 3 feet (90 cm) tall, stems single or branched.
Flowerheads: in flat-topped or slightly rounded inflorescences, very small, white. Ray florets few, inconspicuous.
Leaves: to 8" (20 cm) long and 4" (10 cm) wide, tapering into long petioles, elliptical to broadly ovate, soft hairy, crenate-serrate.

The names feverfew and wild quinine indicate that the plant was used medicinally.

Parthenium, Greek, from *parthenos,* "virgin" for the unusual fact that the disk flowers are sterile; *integrifolium,* Latin, "entire leaved."

Asteraceae (Disk and Ray Flowers)

Parthenium hispidum Hairy Feverfew
May–Oct.

Habitat: limestone glades and prairies of Ozarks. Very similar to *P. integrifolium* but entire plant is covered with long, soft hair.

hispidus, Latin, "hairy."

Polymnia canadensis (48) Leaf-cup, Small Flower Leaf-cup
May–Oct.

Habitat: limestone outcroppings and loose rubble of southern and central Missouri. Tall, straight, growing to 5 feet (1.5 m) tall.
Flowerheads: single or few in open clusters. Ray florets white, short with toothed ends, usually 8; disk yellow, sterile.
Leaves: pinnately 3–5 lobed, bluish green, very soft, lobes toothed, on long petioles, which may show a few tiny sections of leaf tissue. The leaves have a distinct scent when crushed.

Polymnia, Greek, named after the nymph Polyhymnia.

Polymnia uvedalia Yellow Flower Leaf-cup
July–Sept.

Habitat: low woods, base of limestone bluffs, southern and southeastern Missouri. Spreading to 10 feet (3 m) tall.
Flowerheads: open, often leafy cymes, yellow, about 1¾" (5 cm) across.
Leaves: usually 3-lobed, very large to 1 foot (30 cm) long, hairy; leaf tissue extending to winged petiole, palmate.

uvedalia, for Robert Uvedale, 1642–1722, who grew the species in a garden in England.

Ratibida pinnata (71) Gray-head Coneflower
May–Sept.

Habitat: prairies, meadows, waste places, roadsides and railroads; statewide except Southeast Lowlands.
Flowerheads: a few (3–7) drooping ray florets, to 3" (7½ cm) long. The disk rises conelike above the petticoat of the rays.
Leaves: pinnately divided into 3–7 segments, narrow lanceolate, toothed.

Ratibida, the name has no explanation; *pinnata,* Latin, "pinnate" (the leaves).

Rudbeckia hirta (69) Black-eyed Susan
May–Oct.

Habitat: open woods, waste places, roadsides, rock outcroppings, railroads; statewide. To 2½ feet (75 cm) tall, unbranched, very hairy.

Asteraceae (Disk and Ray Flowers)

Flowerheads: normally 1, terminal on a stalk, rays rich yellow, sometimes going into orange, of 10–20 rays, to 4" (10 cm) across. Disk egg-shaped, deep brown to purple-brown.

Leaves: hairy, sessile except a few basal leaves, lanceolate, toothed or not. Botanists are (as usual) divided if the species should be subdivided.

Rudbeckia, named after botanist Olaf Rudbeck, (1630–1702), professor at Upsala, Sweden and teacher of Linnaeus, and possibly also for his son, also named Olaf, also a botany professor at Upsala (1660–1740); **hirta,** Latin, "hairy."

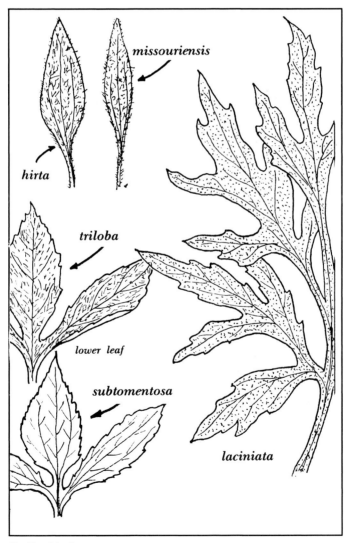

Rudbeckia leaves

Asteraceae (Disk and Ray Flowers)

Rudbeckia missouriensis Missouri Black-eyed Susan
June–Oct.

Habitat: mainly limestone glades and other dry, rocky places in the Ozarks and north to Missouri River. Much like *R. hirta,* but usually smaller and very hairy.

Leaves: linear, only the lowest ones lanceolate.

Rudbeckia triloba (71) Brown-eyed Susan
June–Nov.

Habitat: low, wet woods, roadsides, edges of woods, streamsides, valleys; statewide except Southeast Lowlands. Much-branched stems to 5 feet (1.5 m) tall.
Flowerheads: numerous, much smaller than other *Rudbeckias,* to 1" (25 mm) across. Rays 8-12, bright yellow; disk dark brown. Ray florets with a ring of maroon-red around the disk have been found.
Leaves: only the lower are 3-lobed and have been shed prior to flowering. The others lanceolate, both types with coarse teeth, hairy.

triloba, Latin, "3-lobed."

Rudbeckia subtomentosa Sweet Coneflower
July–Oct.

Habitat: moist places near streams, prairies, roadsides; statewide. Tall, branched, to 6 feet (1.8 m), stems densely hairy above.
Flowerheads: large, about 2" (5 cm) across, with 12-20 yellow rays; disk brown to purple-brown, half-domed.
Leaves: near base, often 3-lobed, the upper ovate, both with large teeth and very hairy.

subtomentosa, Latin, "somewhat hairy."

Rudbeckia laciniata Wild Goldenglow, Tall Coneflower
July–Sept.

Habitat: valleys near streams, low, moist areas; statewide except Southeast Lowlands. Rank-growing, usually unbranched, to 9 feet (2.7 m), covering large bottomland sections.
Flowerheads: few; differ from other *Rudbeckias* by having a green disk and only 6-10 yellow rays.
Leaves: deeply divided nearly to midrib, long petioled, with 3-7 segments and a variety of teeth and lobes; to 10" (25 cm) long and 6" (15 cm) wide. Upper leaves much smaller, often 3-lobed, with or without teeth.

laciniata, Latin, "deeply cut" (the leaves).

Asteraceae (Disk and Ray Flowers)

Senecio Key (based on leaves)

1a) Basal leaves usually present
   2a) leaves rounded, spoon-shaped . . . . *obovatus*
   2b) leaves heart-shaped . . . . *aureus*
   2c) leaves pointed, paddle-shaped . . . . *plattensis*
1b) No basal leaves
   2d) leaves pinnate, lobed with teeth . . . . *glabellus*

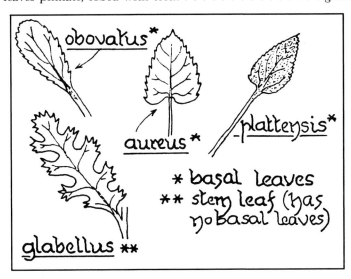

Senecio leaves

Senecio obovatus (59) Squaw-weed, Round-leaved Groundsel
April–June

Habitat: rich or rocky woods, bases of bluffs, on slopes, mostly south of Missouri River. Perennial, to 2 feet (60 cm) tall, generally found in colonies.

Flowerheads: terminal on a long stalk with few leaves, small, yellow. Few rays, looking somewhat ragged.

Leaves: mostly basal, rounded to spoon-shaped, toothed, the leaf tissue conspicuously continued into the petiole, to 3½" (9 cm) long. Stem leaves few, sessile, often deeply lobed.

Senecio, Latin, "old man," possibly for the white-tufted seeds; *obovatus,* Latin, "oblong ovate."

Senecio aureus Golden Ragwort
April–June

Habitat: low, moist areas, near springs, generally south of Missouri River. To 2½ feet (75 cm) tall.

Asteraceae (Disk and Ray Flowers)

Flowerheads: numerous, similar to *S. obovatus.*
Leaves: mostly basal, on very long petioles, heart-shaped, coming to a point, crenate to coarsely toothed. Stem leaves very few, small, pinnate.

aureus, Latin, "golden."

Senecio plattensis Prairie Ragwort
May–June

Habitat: prairies, dry uplands, scattered throughout state. About 2 feet (60 cm) tall, hairy.
Flowerheads: few to many, terminal, with few rays, yellow.
Leaves: mostly basal on long petioles, paddle-shaped, tapering or abruptly contracted to the petiole. Stem leaves few, sessile, short, clasping. Both types sharply toothed.

plattensis, Latin, "of the River Platte."

Senecio glabellus Butterweed
April–June

Habitat: floodplains of Mississippi and Missouri rivers and their tributaries, in southeast and east-central Missouri. An impressive, unbranched plant to 3 feet (90 cm) tall, smooth, without hairs; at times covering acres of floodplain.
Flowerheads: abundant, with rich, golden heads of few rays.
Leaves: on stems only, pinnate, deeply lobed with rounded teeth, reminiscent of the *Acanthus* leaves of Corinthian capitals.

glabellus, Latin, "smooth" (not hairy).

Silphium perfoliatum (75) Cup Plant, Cup Rosin Weed, *July–Sept.*   Carpenter's Weed

Habitat: meadows, low areas near water, waste places; statewide. To 8 feet (2.4 m) tall, with square stems.
Flowerheads: numerous, yellow, with 20–30 rays, variable in size to 2" (5.5 cm) across.
Leaves: mostly opposite, to 1 foot (30 cm), joined around the stem, forming a cup that holds water; wavy margins, rough on both sides, oval to triangular, covered with dots.

Rosin weed is a name given to several *Silphiums,* as they contain a sticky rosin. Carpenter's weed alludes to the square stems.

Silphium, ancient name of a resinous plant, chosen by Linnaeus; *perfoliatum,* Latin, "through the leaf," (i.e. the stem).

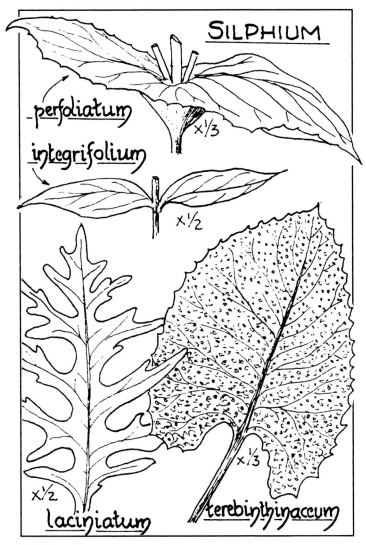

Silphium leaves

Silphium terebinthinaceum (75) Prairie Dock
July–Sept.

Habitat: glades, prairies, roadsides, usually on limestone in Ozarks, central and northeastern Missouri. The flower stalk with only bractlike leaflets to 10 feet (3 m) tall, very slender.

Flowerheads: one to few in an open inflorescence on a long, delicate stem; yellow, with 12–20 rays.

Asteraceae (Disk and Ray Flowers)

Leaves: basal, very large, heart-shaped with coarse teeth on a long petiole, rough on the surface like sandpaper. The leaves develop all summer, while the flowers stalk rises in early fall.

terebinthinaceum, Greek, "with terpentine," the rosin which gives the species a pleasant scent.

Silphium integrifolium Rosin Weed
July–Sept.

Habitat: prairies, fields, roadsides, borders of woods; statewide. Often in colonies, to 7 feet (2.1 m), stems with few hairs or glabrous.
Flowerheads: open to fairly closed inforescences, numerous, yellow, to 2" (5.5 cm) across.
Leaves: mostly opposite, rough, without stalks, (but not surrounding the stem), ovate-lanceolate, with few or no teeth. Plant contains a resinous juice.

integrifolium, Latin, "entire-leaved."

Silphium laciniatum Compass Plant
July–Sept.

Habitat: prairies, fields, glades, roadsides, absent from southeast bottomlands. Tall and showy, to 8 feet (2.1 m), with hairy stems.
Flowerheads: few to many in a narrow, racemelike inflorescence, yellow, to about 2½" (6 cm) across.
Leaves: deeply cleft almost to midrib, huge—to 16" (40 cm), but much shorter toward top of stems, irregularly lobed. The lower leaves turn their edges toward north and south in full sun, therefore "compass plant." Upper stems contain a gummy substance used by Indians as chewing gum.

laciniatum, Latin, "deeply cut" or "lacerated."

Solidago Missouri has 25 species of goldenrod, often difficult to identify. Two species have been chosen as representative. Flowers are insect pollinated and do not release significant amounts of pollen into the air. Thus, they do NOT cause hayfever.

Solidago juncea (74) Early Goldenrod
June–Oct.

Habitat: prairies; dry, open, rocky woods, usually on acid soils; Ozark region north to St. Louis. Stout stalks to 4 feet (1.2 m) tall, branching near top into curved, flower-bearing branchlets.
Leaves: willowlike, narrow, variably toothed, closely or widely spaced. Lower leaves to 12" (30 cm) long, becoming shorter toward top.

juncea, Latin, "like a rush."

Asteraceae (Disk and Ray Flowers)

Solidago speciosa (77) Showy Goldenrod
Aug.-Nov.

Habitat: prairies, meadows, open woods; scattered statewide except Ozark region. Unbranched, to 3 feet (90 cm) tall. Possibly the showiest of Missouri goldenrod.
Flowerheads: spiral around stalk and terminal with fairly large heads (for goldenrods!).
Leaves: alternate, lanceolate, long-pointed, with stems and crenate teeth.

speciosa, Latin, "showy" or "good-looking."

Verbesina Key (based on ray florets)

1a) rays very small, white . . . . *virginica*
1b) rays 2–8, drooping, yellow . . . . *alternifolia*
1c) rays 8–15, horizontal, yellow . . . . *helianthoides*

Verbesina virginica (52) White Crownbeard, Wing-Stem,
Aug.-Oct.   Frostweed

Habitat: open woods, valleys, streamsides south of Missouri River. Perennial with winged stalks to 7 feet (2.1 m) tall. Wings are extension of leaf tissue (decurrent).
Flowerheads: small, clustered terminally, 1–1½" (2.5–4 cm) across with few (1–5) rays, white.
Leaves: alternate, ovate lanceolate, to 7" (18 cm) long with widely spaced, small teeth.

One of 3 plants in Missouri producing "frost-flowers." During the early, hard freezes of the season water is squeezed out through cracks in the stem, freezes and forms spectacular ribbons or crusts of ice.

Verbesina, according to Linnaeus a printer's error for *Forbesina* (Gleason).

Verbesina alternifolia Yellow Ironweed
Aug.-Oct.

Habitat: moist, low woods, streamsides; statewide. To 80" (2 m) tall, similar to *V. virginica.*
Flowerheads: yellow, numerous, the ragged-looking rays (2–8) drooping.
Leaves: ovate to lanceolate, to 10" (25 cm) long, slightly toothed, the stems decurrent.

alternifolia, Latin, "alternately leaved."

Asteraceae (Disk and Ray Flowers)

Verbesina helianthoides (70) Crownbeard, Wing-Stem
May–Oct.

Habitat: open woods, fields, roadsides, railroads, south of Missouri River and east-central counties. Lower than the other *Verbesinas*, to 40" (1 m) rarely taller, with hairy, winged stems.
Flowerheads: few, yellow, with 8-15 rays spreading horizontally and varying in length.
Leaves: coarsely hairy on upper surface, ovate-lanceolate, 2½-6" (6-15 cm) long, alternate, with widely spaced, small teeth.

helianthoides, Latin, "like a sunflower."

Ambrosia differs from all other Composites treated in this book because "male" and "female" flowers are in separate flowerheads on the same plant (monoecious). Until recently they were treated as a separate family, the *Ambrosiaceae.* How the food of the Greek gods got to be the name of this genus is a mystery.

Ambrosia trifida (83) Giant Ragweed, Horse Weed
July–Sept.

Habitat: rich soil on fields, waste places, roadsides; statewide. Much-branched annual to 6 feet (1.8 m) tall, sometimes taller. Growing by the thousands in bottomlands.
Flowerheads: "male" heads quite small, greenish, in loose, terminal racemes; "female" heads, below male heads, nearly hidden in leaf axils.
Leaves: opposite, palmately 3- to 5-divided, (or at times undivided), the lobes pointed with fine teeth, rough, hairy (scabrous).
Seeds: important food for quail, doves, prairie chickens, ducks, pheasants, turkeys and raccoons. Deer browse the leaves. Prehistoric man cultivated ragweed. The seeds of cultivated plants were larger than those of wild species.

The ragweeds are major contributors to hay fever through their wind-carried pollen.

trifida, Latin, "three-lobed."

Ambrosia artemisiifolia Common Ragweed
July–Nov.

Habitat: fields, waste places, roadsides; statewide. Much shorter than the preceding species, to 2½ feet (75 cm).
Flowerheads: the floral arrangement is similar to *A. trifida* with the heads much smaller.
Leaves: rather ornamental, twice pinnatifid, each leaf with many nearly opposite leaflets, the leaflets deeply lobed. Crushed leaves have a strong scent.

artemisiifolia, Latin, "with a leaf of an artemisia."

186

Touch-Me-Not Family *Balsaminaceae*

Soft, watery herbs of temperate and tropical zones, with four genera and 500–600 species, nearly all in genus *Impatiens* (touch-me-not). For floral description of Missouri species, see below. Some species are cultivated. Missouri has one genus with two species.

Impatiens capensis (68) Spotted Touch-Me-Not, Jewelweed
May–Oct.

Habitat: damp, low woods, streamsides, swampy places, bottoms of ravines; statewide. Soft plants to 5 feet (1.5 m) tall, much-branched with watery stems.
Flowers: like a cornucopia, 3 unequal sepals, 2 of them small, the third a sack with a spur; 5 petals, appearing as 3 (as the laterals are joined), each with 2 lobes; stamens joined to the stigma; orange, each hanging from a slender stem.
Leaves: alternate, soft, egg-shaped, bluish green, coarsely toothed, to 3½" (9 cm) long.
Fruit: a slender capsule which, in drying, contracts, coils and splits explosively, casting seeds far away in all directions.

It is widely believed that rubbing leaves and stems of *Impatiens* on the skin will prevent and even cure poison ivy (*Rhus radicans*) infection.

Impatiens, Latin, "impatient"; *capensis* refers to the Cape of Good Hope, probably an error.

Impatiens pallida Pale Touch-me-not
May–Oct.

Entirely like *I. capensis*, but flowers are pale yellow and the spur points downward at right angle.

pallida, Latin, "pale."

Barberry Family *Berberidaceae*

Mostly shrubs, some perennial herbs in north temperate regions, with 13–16 genera and 550–600 species. Floral characteristics vary widely and the family exists more for technical reasons than floral similarities. Ornamentals are barberry, mahonia and nandina with many cultivars. Missouri has 3 genera with one species each.

Podophyllum peltatum (27) May Apple, Mandrake
March–May

Habitat: moist or dry, open woods, sometimes persisting in fields adjacent to woods; statewide.

187

Flower: single flowers develop only on plants with 2 leaves from the axil of the leaf stems, white, with 6-9 waxy, spreading petals, a green, clublike pistil, to 3" (8 cm) across. A rare pink form exists.

Leaves: Large, to 1 foot with many deep notches to near middle of leaf, the segments with coarse teeth, arising from a smooth stem, 1-1½ feet (30-45 cm) tall.

Fruit: the "may apple," egg-shaped and egg-sized, botanically a berry, edible with a pleasant taste.

Leaves and roots are poisonous but have medicinal use.

Podophyllum Greek, "foot-leaf," *peltatum*, Latin, "shield-shaped," both referring to the leaves.

Trumpet Creeper FAMILY *Bignoniaceae*

Some 120 genera and 650 species, mostly tropical climbers, some shrubs and trees, with a few species in temperate zone of North America. Large, tube-shaped flowers in clusters, 5-lobed and four stamens (sometimes reduced to two) inserted in tube under upper lip or lobe. Missouri has three genera with one native species each (*Catalpa, Bignonia,* and *Campsis*)

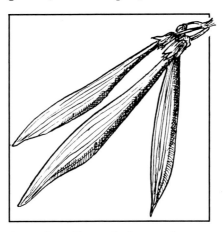

Campsis radicans, fruit; actual length 6".

Campsis radicans (63) Trumpet Vine, Trumpet Creeper, *May-Aug.*   Cow-itch

Habitat: thickets, open woods, fencerows, waste places, roadsides, railroads; statewide. An aggressive vine with aerial rootlets on stems which become woody with age.

Flowers: tube-shaped in terminal clusters, 5-lobed, to 3" (8 cm) long, orange, red-orange, rarely red. The flowers are favored by hummingbirds.

Leaves: compound, with 6–10 opposite (and one terminal) leaflets, ovate-lanceolate, coarsely toothed, with long points.

Some people get a poison-ivy type rash after touching the plant, thus "cow-itch."

Campsis, Greek, "curved" (the stamens); *radicans,* Latin, "rooting" (the aerial rootlets).

Borage Family *Boraginaceae*

In all temperate and subtropical areas, about 100 genera and 2,000 species. For floral arrangements see page 12. Includes forget-me-not (*Myosotis*) and heliotrope (*Heliotropium*). Missouri has 10 genera with 17 species, all quite hairy with the exception of the bluebells (*Mertensia virginica*).

Cynoglossum virginianum (111) Wild Comfrey, Giant Forget-Me-Not
April–June

Habitat: wooded slopes or bottomlands, central and southeast Missouri. Flower stalks to 2½ feet (75 cm) tall with a few clasping leaves.
Flowers: like small forget-me-not in a washed-out sky-blue to greenish white, small tubes ending in 5 rounded lobes, about ½" (12 mm) across.
Leaves: mostly basal, elliptical with long petioles, very hairy, soft stems to 1 foot (30 cm) long; leaves few, clasping the hairy stems.
Fruit: 4 round nutlets, hairy, depressed on upper surface, clinging to man and beast.

Cynoglossum, Greek, "dog" and Latin, "tongue" (the basal leaves).

Echium vulgare (114) Viper's Bugloss, Blue-Weed
May–Sept.

Habitat: moist or dry places, gravel bars, ditches, waste places, roadsides, disturbed soil; north, eastern and central Missouri. Native of Europe.
Flowers: along upper stalks in 1-sided spikes in an unfurling, tight coil; funnel-shaped with uneven lobes to ¾" (20 mm) long; pink in bud, blue to ultramarine later with pink stamens protruding. A white form exists but has not been found in Missouri.
Leaves: linear-oblong, sessile, extremely white, hairy (as are the stems), giving the plant a silvery appearance.

Bugloss is an English word given to a number of plants of the Borage Family in Europe.

Echium, Greek, "viper," a fancied resemblance of the fruit-nutlet to a snake's head; *vulgare,* Latin, "common."

Boraginaceae

Lithospermum canescens (54) Hoary or Orange Puccoon
March–June

Habitat: glades, edges of woods, fields, roadsides; statewide except Southeast Lowlands. Many stalks from 1 root system, 6–12" (15–30 cm) tall. Starts flowering very low to the ground.

Flowers: tubular, though this is hardly visible, with 5 lobes, many from coiled inflorescences, terminal, orange-yellow, rarely pale yellow.

Leaves: inconspicuous at flowering time, alternate, lanceolate, pointing upward, very hairy.

Lithospermum, litho-, Greek, "stone," *-spermum,* Latin "seed"; *canescens,* Latin, "gray-hairy." "Puccoon" is an Indian name; native Americans are supposed to have used the flowers for a dye.

Lithospermum incisum Yellow Puccoon
April–June

Habitat: fields, roadsides, glades, sometimes in moist places, scattered in central and western Missouri. Very similar to *L. canescens* but flowers have lobes with teeth and are bright yellow rather than orange.

incisum, Latin, "incised," the flower lobes.

Lithospermum arvense Corn Gromwell
April–June

Habitat: fields, waste places, roadsides, missing from northern and southernmost counties. Very different from the yellow-flowering puccoons above. Rough, hairy annual, to 18" (45 cm) tall.

Flowers: tiny, almost hidden by bracts, white with 5 lobes; reminiscent of forget-me-not, a relative.

Leaves: alternate, linear, very hairy, sessile.

arvense, Latin, "of cultivated fields."

Mertensia virginica (107) Bluebells, Virginia Cowslip
March–June

Habitat: bottomlands of rich woods, low, wooded hillsides; scattered statewide except northwest and southwest. Fleshy, showy plants to 2 feet (60 cm) tall, often in large groups.

Flowers: many in loose clusters, terminal, hanging bell-like about 1" (2.5 cm) long. Buds pink, turn to light blue on opening. Pink forms are not rare; a white form exists.

Leaves: lower leaves are long, tapering into stems, broad, ovate to 5" (13 cm) long; stem leaves smaller, elliptical. All leaves blue-green.

This is the only Missouri member of the Borage Family which is NOT hairy.

Mertensia, for Franz Carl Mertens (1764–1831), a German botanist.

Mertensia virginica; actual length 1".

Mustard Family *Brassicaceae* (Cruciferae)

The Mustard Family contains about 380 genera with 3,000 species of worldwide distribution. For floral details see page 10. Food plants: cabbage, broccoli, turnip, radish, watercress, mustard; rape provides oil. Many species are weeds. Missouri has 27 genera with 54 species, 17 of them introduced, not counting roadway and railroad adventives, probably killed by now by herbicide spraying.

Barbarea vulgaris (58) Yellow Rocket, Winter Cress
April–June

Habitat: fields, cultivated and fallow, waste places, roadsides, railroads; statewide. Native of Europe. A leafy, much-branched weed to 2 feet (60 cm) tall.
Flowers: many, crowded, bright yellow with the typical 4 petals in cross position, about 1/3" (8 mm) across.
Leaves: featherlike, the terminal section much larger than the sections below, the lower on long petioles; stem leaves often sessile.
Fruit: a long seedpod which forms as flowering continues (a silique).

Barbarea, named for Ste. Barbara; *vulgaris,* Latin, "common."

Brassica nigra (58) Black Mustard
April–Nov.

Habitat: fields, waste places, roadsides; scattered statewide. A coarse weed to 5 feet (1.5 m) tall, either branched or not, annual. Native of Eurasia.
Flowers: very small, yellow, 4-petaled (see above as for *Barbarea*).
Leaves: on long petioles, highly variable, often irregularly lobed to midrib, generally ovate, some with teeth.
Fruit: same as for *Barbarea,* above.

Brassicaceae

Many kinds of mustards have escaped from cultivation; all are immigrants with a great variety of leaf shapes.

Brassica, the classical Latin name for cabbage; ***nigra,*** Latin, "black" (the seeds).

Capsella bursa-pastoris (25) Shepherd's Purse
March–Nov.

Habitat: waste places, roadsides, gardens, almost any open habitat. Native of Europe. Many-stemmed weed to 2 feet (6 dm) tall.

Flowers: many along upper part of stems and their branches, white, minute, with 4 rounded petals.

Leaves: basal form a rosette, deeply lobed, similar to dandelion but much smaller, to 4" (10 cm) long; stem leaves small, lanceolate.

Fruit: the fancied shape of a shepherd's purse, 2-lobed, heart-shaped, formed while flowering continues. Young leaves esteemed in salads and, without dressing, by poultry.

Capsella bursa-pastoris, Latin, "little shepherd's purse."

Cardamine bulbosa (28) Spring Cress
March–June

Habitat: wet places, springs and spring branches; southern and east-central counties. Low, spreading, to 12" (30 cm) tall.

Flowers: small, 4-petaled, white, terminal in small clusters.

Leaves: of 2 kinds: when rooted in water the stem leaves are narrow-lanceolate; when rooted in wet earth leaves are triangular with some teeth, the lower on long petioles, the upper to nearly sessile. Basal leaves are rounded on long stems.

Cardamine, Greek, "cress." The common name spring cress should not be confused with water cress (*Nasturtium officinale*); ***bulbosa,*** Latin, "with a bulb."

Cardamine parviflora Small-Flowered Bitter Cress
March–July

Habitat: upland, rocky woods, ridges; scattered statewide. Mostly single stems with little or no branching, to 12" (30 cm) tall.

Flowers: same as for *C. bulbosa.*

Leaves: basal and stem with 3–6 pair of opposite, small lobes spaced along the leaf rib, the terminal having the same nearly linear shape.

Seedpods: long and very slender.

parviflora, Latin, "small-flowered."

Cardamine pensylvanica Bitter Cress
March–July

Habitat: moist places of many kinds in central and southern counties. Stems single or spreading, to 2 feet (6 dm) tall.
Flowers: same as *C. bulbosa.*
Leaves: similar to *C. parviflora* but larger and the lobes are connected by leaf tissue along the midrib of the leaf.

Dentaria laciniata (26) Toothwort
March–May

Habitat: slopes of woods or wooded valleys; statewide except Southeast Lowlands. Never in large groups but quite common through woods in early spring. Single stem, to 16" (40 cm) tall.
Flowers: toward top of stem, several, white, sometimes pale lavender, fairly large with the characteristic 4 petals of the family borne above the whorl of leaves.
Leaves: in a whorl, midway on the plant stem, divided into 3 deeply incised sections which are pointed and coarsely toothed, giving a 5-lobed appearance.
Root: a small tuber.

Dentaria, Latin, "tooth-flower"; *laciniata,* Latin, "torn" (the leaves).

Erysimum capitatum (61) Western Wall Flower
May–July

Habitat: limestone bluffs, rocky, open hillsides in full sun; scattered in valleys of central Missouri. Starts flowering on stems 12" (30 cm) high, growing to 40" (1 m) while blooming. Stems single or branched.
Flowers: about ½" (1.3 cm) across, bright orange with 4 petals, an outstanding perfume.
Leaves: sessile, slightly toothed, linear, alternate along the stems.

This is a biennial or winter-annual and cannot be relied on to appear each year. It often disappears after a year of a fine display. Other *Erysimum* species in Missouri are much less showy.

Erysimum, Greek, ancient name for hedge mustard; *capitatum,* Latin, "headed" (the inflorescence).

Lepidium campestre (29) Field Cress, Pepper Grass
April–June

Habitat: fields, waste places, roadsides, railroads; statewide. Native of Europe. Densely hairy stems, usually 10–18" (25–45 cm) tall, much-branched toward top.
Flowers: typical Mustard Family with 4 small petals, white, arising from the many upper branches.

Leaves: the basal dandelionlike with rounded tops, short; stem leaves ascending, about 1¼" (4 cm) long, entire, clasping the stem and having 2 pointed ears.

Fruit: the almost round, fairly large seedpods (botanically, a silicle) with 2 seeds each are ornamental due to their quantity, and are appreciated by birds. Pepper grass in fruit looks like a candelabra. The plant has a gray appearance due to the fire hairiness.

Lepidium, Greek, "small scale," the thin seed capsules; *campestre,* Latin, "of the field."

Lepidium virginicum Pepper Grass
March–Nov.

Habitat: fields, waste places, roadsides, railroads; statewide. Stems NOT hairy, to 20" (5 dm) tall, much-branched near top.

Flowers: same as for *L. campestre.*

Leaves: the basal featherlike, sharply toothed; stem leaves do NOT clasp the stem; narrow lanceolate to linear with a few pronounced teeth.

The name pepper grass is given to a number of species of the Mustard Family.

Nasturtium officinale (31) Water Cress
April–Oct.

Habitat: in and around springs and spring-branches in southern and central Missouri. Usually found growing in water, rising out of it in bushy plants to 10" (25 cm) tall.

Flowers: masses at terminals, minute, with the 4 tiny petals white, sometimes tinged lavender.

Leaves: dissected with a rounded blade at the top and several opposite, rounded lobes below along the leaf axis.

Water cress is used as a salad and has a tangy flavor. With our general stream pollution, care must be taken that plants taken for human consumption come from an uncontaminated source. Water cress is also often host to masses of aphids.

Nasturtium, "Monk's Latin" for "nose twister," referring to the sharp, mustardlike taste; *officinale,* Latin, indicates that the plant has had medicinal application in the past.

Cactus Family *Cactaceae*

A nearly all-American family of 87 genera with over 2,000 species. All genera but 1 are succulent, leaves reduced or eliminated, while swollen stems contain chlorophyll, an adaptation to dry conditions. Many species are spined, have showy flowers with sepals and petals looking alike, and many stamens. Size varies from small buttons to tree-sized saguaros. Prickly pears are cultivated for their fruit. Missouri has 2 species.

Opuntia compressa (64) Prickly Pear
May–July

Habitat: glades, rocky, open hillsides, valleys, roadsides in south and central Missouri. A low, spreading plant.
Flowers: numerous, yellow, with many matching sepals and petals, the innermost often with a bright orange splotch, to 3" (7.5 cm) across, with many stamens.
Leaves: the large, paddle-shaped green parts are NOT leaves but thickened stems. These have tiny, soft protuberances (the real leaves) distributed over the surface, each surrounded by spines and hairlike bristles which are very difficult to remove from the skin once they are embedded. These leaves persist only a short time.
Fruit: edible, purplish red, pear-shaped with tufts or bristles.
Seeds: embedded in a mucilaginous substance.

Opuntia, a name used by Pliny 1,500 years before the discovery of America. Since nearly all cacti are of American origin, the name must have been applied to another plant; *compressa*, Latin, "compressed" (the leaflike stems).

Bellflower Family *Campanulaceae*

Consists of 2 subfamilies of about 35 genera and 600 species, treated as distinct families by many authors; *Campanuloideae* with bell-like flowers, and the *Lobelioideae* of worldwide distribution but centered in tropics, with flowers of an upper and lower lip. Missouri has three genera and 12 species.

Campanula americana (116) Tall Bellflower
June–Oct.

Habitat: moist, open woods, streamsides, creeks, variable; statewide. Tall, straight stalk, usually branched, to 6 feet (1.8 m), often still seen in winter.
Flowers: not bell-shaped, on a very long spike, light blue to rarely white. The lobes of a very short tube, large, spreading. Flowers have a white ring at center, a protruding pistil with 4 lobes, and prominent linear bracts; they open without any apparent sequence along the stalk.
Leaves: 3–6" (7½–15 cm) long, lanceolate, sessile or with very short stems.

C. americana is an easy garden subject, spreading through seed dispersal.

Campanula, Latin, "little bell," the typical floral shape of members of the genus.

Campanulaceae

Lobelia spicata (40) Spiked Lobelia
May–Aug.

Habitat: open woods, streamsides, sloughs, ponds; statewide. Single stalk to 3 feet (90 cm) tall.

Flowers: spikelike racemes along top of stem, about 1/3" (1 cm) long, with a 2-divided upper lip and a 3-divided lower lip, bluish to dull white; subtended by a bractlike, linear leaflet.

Leaves: alternate, spaced apart to 3½" (9 cm) long, lanceolate, slightly toothed, much smaller toward top of stem.

Lobelia, named for the 16th century herbalist Mathias von Lobel; *spicata,* Latin, "with a spike."

Lobelia inflata Indian Tobacco
June–Oct.

Habitat: fields, waste places, open woods; statewide. Stems usually branched, to 3 feet (90 cm) tall.

Flowers: very small, as for *L. spicata,* pale light blue or white.

Leaves: ovate to oblong, toothed, hairy, to 2½" (6½ cm) long.

Fruit: the ovaries become inflated as seeds ripen and are readily visible.

Plant contains a narcotic poison and was formerly used in medicine.

inflata, Latin, "inflated."

Lobelia siphilitica (117) Blue or Great Lobelia
Aug.–Oct.

Habitat: wet places, streamsides, ditches, sloughs, lakes; statewide. Unbranched or much-branched stalks to 3 feet (90 cm) tall, rarely much taller.

Flowers: in leaf axils of upper stem leaves, of typical *Lobelia* shape with 2-parted upper lip and 3-divided lower lip to 1" (2½ cm) long, with an extended flowering season; color variable, light or dark violet, light or dark blue or lavender, rarely white.

Leaves: alternate, light green, narrow lance-shaped, 2-6" (5-15 cm) long, sometimes with few open spaced teeth.

Plant contains a narcotic poison and was formerly used in medicine.

siphilitica, in the 18th century it was believed in Europe that extracts of *L. siphilitica* were a remedy for veneral disease, giving the species its name.

Lobelia cardinalis (102) Cardinal Flower
July–Oct.

Habitat: same as for *L. siphilitica* but usually not found growing together; south and central Missouri. Stalks at first unbranched, to 5 feet (1.5 m), later with many flowering side branches.

Flowers: in dense racemes, terminal with slender, leaflike bracts; arise from upper leaf axils. Floral description as for *L. siphilitica* but of cardinal-red color with protruding stamens, rarely vermillion, very rarely white.

Leaves: alternate, numerous, dark green to 6" (15 cm) long, lance-shaped, finely toothed.

> *cardinalis,* Latin, "of a cardinal" (the color).

Specularia perfoliata (109) Venus' Looking Glass
April–Aug.

Habitat: fields, waste places, streamsides; statewide. Usually single-stemmed, averaging 18" (45 cm).

Flowers: surrounded by slender, leaflike bracts; emerge from leaf axils; star-shaped, about ½" (1.2 cm) across, blue-purple, rarely white. Those on lower parts of stem do not open but produce seeds.

Leaves: round, palmately veined, clasping the stem.

> *Specularia,* Latin, "mirror," the name given to an unknown European plant for an also unknown reason; *perfoliata,* Latin, "through the stem" (the clasping leaves).

Honeysuckle Family *Caprifoliaceae*

About 18 genera and 450 species of shrubs and climbers and a few herbs and trees, mostly in tropical and temperate North America and Eurasia. Flowers regular or irregular, mostly tubes with 5 spreading lobes in many shapes. Some 50 forms of *Viburnum* are used in horticulture. Missouri has five genera with 17–20 species; some may be extinct.

Lonicera flava (57) Yellow Honeysuckle
April–May

Habitat: openings and borders of woods, streamsides in Ozarks. A woody, trailing, climbing or sometimes shrublike honeysuckle.

Flowers: 1" (2.5 cm) long tubes with protruding stamens, in terminal clusters above a platterlike union of 2 joined leaves that clasp the stem, orange or orange-yellow.

Leaves: opposite, sessile, thick, egg-shaped with a gray underside.

Fruit: a red berry esteemed by birds.

> *Lonicera* named for Adam Lonitzer, a German physician and naturalist of the 16th century; *flava,* Latin, "yellow."

Lonicera sempervirens Trumpet Honeysuckle
April–May

Habitat: roadsides, streambanks, thickets in central and southern counties. Escaped from cultivation. A climbing plant.

Caprifoliaeae

Flowers: typical honeysuckle, stamens and pistil NOT protruding from tube, deep red on outside, yellow inside.
Leaves: paddle-shaped, pointed toward base, entire, opposite, the uppermost joined at their base.

sempervirens, Latin, "evergreen," the status of the plant in southern areas.

Lonicera japonica Japanese Honeysuckle
May–June

Habitat: fencerows, woods, roadsides, railroads in southern and central counties. Native of Asia; escaped from cultivation.
Flowers: white or creamy yellow, to 2" (5 cm) long tubes.
Leaves: opposite (never joined), ovate, to 3" (8 cm) long on very short stems. Young leaves often lobed or irregularly cut.
Fruit: black berries.

An aggressive climber which strangles trees and shrubs often over large areas.

Lonicera prolifera Grape Honeysuckle
April–June

Habitat: open woods, bluffs, thickets, in northern two-thirds of state. Woody climber.
Flowers: in whorls arising on stems from upper leaf axils, pale yellow, small with protruding stamens and pistil.
Leaves: opposite, connected by a broad base, pointed, the upper surface with a white coating (glaucous). The inflorescence subtended by a jointed, large leaf.

prolifera, Latin, "prolific" or "fruitful."

Sambucus canadensis (39) Elderberry
May–July

Habitat: fencerows, ditches, roadsides, railroads, waste places; statewide. Thicket-forming shrub from root runners, with many stems, gray-brown with many pores (stomata), pithy inside, to 10 feet (3 m) tall, rarely a small tree.
Flowers: in an umbrella-shaped cluster, very small with 5 petals and 5 stamens, carried terminal, delicately scented.
Leaves: opposite, compound, 5-11, usually 7 leaflets, lanceolate to ovate, variable, toothed. Lower leaves sometimes 3-divided.
Fruit: many purple-black berries, edible for jellies, winemaking, pies. Birds and animals also eat the berries. Unripe fruit can be used like capers.

Sambucus, the classical name for elder.

Triosteum perfoliatum (86) Horse Gentian, Wild Coffee, *May–July* Tinker's Weed

Habitat: dry, open woods on hillsides or valleys; statewide. Upright stalk to 4 feet (1.2 m) tall.

Flowers: clustered in leaf axils on very short stems, almost hidden by green calix, tubular with 5 small lobes, reddish brown.

Leaves: opposite, joined around the stem (connate), broad lanceolate with smooth margins.

Fruit: berries that resemble little oranges, remaining on the stalks through fall. The dried fruit was used by early Pennsylvania settlers as a coffee substitute.

Triosteum, Greek, shortened by Linneaus from *triostospermum* "3 stony seeds"; *perfoliatum*, Latin, "through the stem" (the leaves).

Triosteum aurantiacum Scarlet-Fruited Horse Gentian *May–July*

Habitat: rich woods; absent from western and southeastern counties. Very similar to *T. perfoliatum*, but leaves are NOT "perfoliate"; narrowing at base to a winged petiole, very hairy.

aurantiacum, Latin, "orange-red."

Viburnum Key (based on leaf characteristics)

1a) Teeth on leaf margins small and crowded
    2a) Leaves thick, leathery with rusty-brown hair on underside or on midrib . . . . *rufidulum*
    2b) Leaves NOT leathery, without hair . . . . *prunifolium*
1b) Teeth on leaf margins large, coarse, triangular . . . *rafinesquianum*

Viburnum rufidulum (32) Southern Black Haw *April–May*

Habitat: dry woods, rich valleys, streamsides; absent from northern Missouri. Shrub or small tree to 20 feet (6 m) tall but usually much shorter.

Flowers: large, terminal clusters of 3- or 4-rayed cymes to 5" (13 cm) across, individually tiny, white, 5-lobed, only ¼" (6 mm) wide.

Leaves: thick, leathery, shiny on upper surface, lighter with rust-colored hair underneath, elliptical ovate, to 3" (8 cm) long; teeth on leaf margins small and crowded. Leaves turn red in fall.

Fruit: a blue-black drupe (a stone-fruit surrounded by soft matter, as in a plum).

Viburnum, a classical Latin name of unknown meaning; *rufidulum*, Latin, "reddish," the lower leaf surfaces.

Viburnum prunifolium Black Haw
April–May

Habitat: dry woods, rich valleys, streamsides; statewide. A non-hairy large shrub, rarely a small tree.
Flowers: as for *V. rufidulum.*
Leaves: opposite on petioles, obtuse (rounded at top), finely toothed, NOT shiny, light green, without hair, not leathery.
Fruit: a blue-black drupe, (see above under *V. rufidulum*).

The shrub provides an outstanding fall color display from lavender to maroon-purple and deep rose-red.

prunifolium, Latin, "with leaves like a plum."

Viburnum rafinesquianum (38) Missouri Viburnum, Downy
May–June   Arrow-Wood

Habitat: wooded bluffs, open woods, streamsides; missing from southeast, east-central and western counties. A small shrub, often as understory in woods, to 5 feet (1.5 m) high.
Flowers: domed clusters to 4" (10 cm) across, very small, white, each with 5 tiny petal-like lobes.
Leaves: more or less triangular, a rounded base and 6–10 coarse, large teeth on each margin. Some are long-pointed. The leaves turn dull purple-red to dull wine-purple in autumn.
Fruit: a blue-black drupe (see above).

rafinesquianum named for Samuel Constantine Rafinesque Schmaltz (1783–1840), a German botanist who spent several years collecting plants in the U.S.

Pink Family *Caryophyllaceae*

About 80 genera with 2,000 species worldwide, but centered in temperate zones and Mediterranean. Leaves usually opposite or in whorls. For floral details see page 12. Carnations are the best known cultivated members, while chickweed may be the least appreciated. Missouri hosts 11 genera with 33 species of which 13 are introduced, plus a few escaped garden subjects.

Dianthus armeria (96) Deptford Pink
May–Oct.

Habitat: fields, pastures, waste places, roadsides; statewide. A stiffly erect annual to 20" (5 dm) tall. Native of Europe; biennial.
Flowers: in small groups (cymes), subtended by long, linear bracts, a green calyx, and 5 fringed petals, pink with white dots.

Leaves: very narrow, linear, to 3" (8 cm) long, opposite and hairy.

Often in large colonies in abandoned fields.

Dianthus, Greek "flower of the gods"; ***armeria,*** probably a word of Celtic origin, "near the sea," for a resemblance to the sea pink.

Saponaria officinalis (101) Soapwort, Bouncing Bet
June–Oct.

Habitat: gravel and sandbars, waste places, roadsides, railroads; statewide. Simple or branched stems, about 2 feet (6 dm) tall. Native of Europe. Often forms large colonies.
Flowers: tight or open groups (cymes), subtended by bracts. A long calyx tube, typical of the family; petals with 1 rounded notch, white or pink, showy, with a delightful fragrance.
Leaves: opposite, elliptical-lanceolate, to 8" (10 cm) long.

Saponaria, Latin, "soap-plant," because the plant contains a mucilaginous juice which forms lather in water; ***officinalis,*** Latin, indicates a medicinal use in the past.

Silene, of 12 species in Missouri, 6 came from Europe and only 3 have a wide distribution. The *Silene* genus produces a sticky juice on its stems which catches insects, thus the common name catchfly.

Silene stellata (48) Starry Campion, Catchfly
June–Sept.

Habitat: dry, wooded uplands and slopes; statewide. Perennial with several stems, usually 2½ feet (7.5 dm) tall.
Flowers: in a loose panicle, subtended by bractlike, small leaves, with a cup-shaped calyx from which 5 white, finely fringed petals protrude. Stamens are long.
Leaves: most of them in whorls of 4, lanceolate to oval-lanceolate, sessile, opposite, to 3" (8 cm) long.

Silene, named for the Greek god Silanos, a slippery character; ***stellata,*** Latin, "star-shaped."

Silene virginica (91) Fire Pink
April–June

Habitat: wooded slopes and valleys of Ozarks and east-central counties. A low perennial with many spreading stems, to 2 feet (6 dm) tall, usually much lower.
Flowers: arise on fairly long stems (peduncles) from upper leaf axils. Calyx a 5-pointed cylindrical tube. Corolla lobes narrow, each with a single notch, brilliant red. Where the lobes open from the tube is a small, crownlike circle of red lobes, the corona (crown), also red. Stamens protrude from corolla.
Leaves: opposite, narrow, to 4" (10 cm) long.

Silene antirrhina Sleepy Catchfly
April–Sept.

Habitat: roadsides, glades, fields, waste places, open woods; statewide. Annual with several stems, the lower part of which is densely hairy, from 8"–2½ feet (10 cm–75 cm) tall. Parts of the stems have a dark, sticky area.
Flowers: numerous, very small, white or light pink.
Leaves: opposite, mostly oblanceolate, to 2" (5 cm) long.

> *antirrhina,* Greek, is also the name of the snapdragon; according to L.H. Bailey "snout flower."

Morning Glory Family *Convolvulaceae*

Some 50 genera with 1,800 species, mostly climbers, but also herbs and shrubs in temperate and tropical zones. For flora details see page 14. Morning glories are cultivated in Japan; *Ipomoea batatas* is the tropical sweet potato (wrongly called yam). Some of our species are hard-to-control weeds, such as the parasitic dodder (*Cuscuta*). Missouri has four genera with 18 species, of which five are introduced.

Convolvulus sepium (39) Hedge Bindweed
May–Sept.

Habitat: fields, waste places, roadsides, railroads; statewide. Creeping and climbing plant, spreading by deep roots, very difficult to eradicate.
Flowers: on long peduncles from leaf axils, large, funnel-shaped, to 2½" (7 cm) long, white or pink with a few white stripes on the inside. Each flower subtended by small oblong bracts.
Leaves: arrow-shaped with 2 squarish lobes, to 4" long (10 cm). Bindweed flowers close by noon on sunny days.

> *Convolvulus,* Latin, "to entwine"; *sepium,* Latin, "of hedges or fences."

Convolvulus arvensis Field or Small Bindweed
May–Sept.

Habitat: fields, waste places, roadsides, railroads; statewide. Native of Europe. Trailing or climbing, forming dense mats.
Flowers: much smaller than *C. sepium.* Two minute bracts an inch or more below flowers, which are on stems arising from the bracts, while *C. sepium* has bracts directly below the flower and only 1 flower. *C. aryensis* has several flowers arising on peduncles from the bract-point. Color white or light pink.
Leaves: triangular, the 2 lower lobes pointed (not squarish as in *C. sepium*).

> *arvensis,* Latin, "of cultivated fields."

Ipomoea pandurata (41) Wild Potato Vine, Man of the Earth
May–Sept.

Habitat: fields, streamsides, roadways, waste places, railroads; statewide. Trailing or climbing vine.
Flowers: in terminal clusters, from 1-7, on long stem, funnel-shaped, to 3" (8 cm) long, white with dark crimson or purple center.
Leaves: on long stems, heart-shaped, pointed, to 6" (15 cm) long.
Root: a tuber to 2 feet (60 cm) long and weighing 20 pounds or more, often branched, leglike.

Indians boiled and ate the tubers.

Ipomoea, a word invented by Linnaeus from 2 Greek words to mean "like a bindweed"; *pandurata,* Latin, "fiddle-shaped," probably referring to some of the leaves.

Dogwood Family *Cornaceae*

A small family of trees and shrubs with 13 genera and 100 species in the north-temperate zone with a few in warmer climates. Leaves usually opposite. Inflorescence often an umbel, sometimes surrounded by showy bracts. Flowers small, 4- or 5-lobed, ovary inferior. Fruit, a drupe or a berry. Missouri has 1 genus, dogwood (*Cornus*) with 6 species.

Cornus Key
1a) Leaves opposite
   2a) flowers surrounded by large white bracts . . . . *florida*
   2b) flowers NOT showing large bracts
      3a) leaves woolly hairy underneath . . . . *drummondii*
      3b) leaves NOT hairy or only slightly so, young branches
      densely hairy . . . . *obliqua*
      3c) leaves NOT hairy or only slightly so, young branches
      without hair . . . . *racemosa*
1b) Leaves alternate . . . . *alternifolia*

Cornus florida (32) Flowering Dogwood
April–May

Habitat: wooded slopes, usually on acid soil, bluffs in counties along Missouri River and south of it. The state tree of Missouri, usually an understory tree in oak-hickory hardwood forests, but specimens with 8" (20 cm) diameter are known. The outstanding trees develop in full sun and excellent drainage, NOT under other trees.
Flowers: in tight clusters of 20-30 with 4 petals and 4 stamens, light yellow, surrounded by 4 large, white bracts, each bract with a terminal notch tipped purplish. Pink bracted trees are a rarity in nature.

Cornaceae

Leaves: opposite, ovate, pointed at both ends, to 5" (13 cm) long with arcuate veining (the veins bent bowlike, parallel to the edges of the leaves).

Fruit: brilliant red drupe, each holding 2 seeds, eaten by birds, especially robins, mockingbirds and turkeys.

Wood: very strong and shock resistant.

> **Do not attempt to transplant dogwood from the wild!** Their roots are severely damaged by digging, weakening the tree, which then is easily attacked by borers.

> *Cornus,* Latin for "horn," because of the wood's hardness.

Cornus florida, flowers with bracts; actual size 3".

Cornus drummondii Rough-leaved Dogwood
May–June

Habitat: usually in dry areas, glades, open woods, sometimes along streams and in wet places; statewide. Shrub varying in height with gray or brownish twigs.

Flowers: many, very small in umbel-like, wide inflorescences, either flat or convex, off-white without bracts.

Leaves: opposite, ovate, pointed, 2-3" (5-8 cm) long, woolly hairs underneath, rough hairs on top.

Fruit: a white drupe on a red stem.

> *drummondii,* for Thomas Drummond, (1807–1835), the discoverer of the shrub.

Cornus obliqua (43) Swamp, Pale, or Silky Dogwood
May-July

Habitat: lowlands in wet areas; statewide except Southeast Lowlands. Shrub to 10 feet (3 m) tall with reddish-brown to dark brown young branches.
Flowers: in open, flat inflorescences, white to creamy white.
Leaves: opposite, narrower than other shrubby dogwoods, conspicuously narrowed at their base, not hairy or only slightly so.
Fruit: drupe, light blue to whitish.

obliqua, Latin, "oblique" or "awry," the shape of the stone fruit.

Cornus racemosa Gray Dogwood
May-July

Habitat: moist ground in lowlands, streamsides, fields, roadsides, fencerows; scattered statewide. Shrub to 16 feet (5 m) tall, forming thickets.
Flowers: small, white, in domed clusters, the domes nearly as high as wide. Flowers can occur on very young plants only 3 feet (90 cm) tall.
Leaves: opposite, very similar to *C. obliqua* but wider, elliptical, long-pointed on long petioles; not hairy or only slightly so. Color turns purple to dull red in fall.
Fruit: white drupe on a red stem.

racemosa, Latin, "flowers in racemes."

Cornus alternifolia Alternate-leaf Dogwood
May-July

Habitat: north-facing wooded slopes and wooded banks of streams; absent from western counties. Shrub or small tree.
Flowers: in dense, domed clusters, small, white.
Leaves: alternate, crowded at ends of branches, appearing whorl-like, pale and whitened on underside, thin, ovate, on petioles, to 2" (5 cm) long but variable even on same branch.
Fruit: blue-black drupe on a reddish stalk.

alternifolia, Latin, "with alternate leaves."

Teasel Family *Dipsacaceae*

Herbs of Eurasia and southern Africa, centered around the Mediterranean, of 11 genera and 350 species. Flowers in dense heads, each flower subtended by bracts, tubular with four or five lobes and 2-4 stamens inserted at base of tube. Distinct from *Compositae* because stamens are **NOT** joined around pistil. *Scabiosa* is a garden subject. In Missouri, *Dipsacus* has two species.

Dipsacus sylvestris (99) Teasel
June–Oct.

Habitat: fields, waste places, roadsides, railroads; in southern and central Missouri. Native of Europe. Stout, straight, prickly and branched stems, to 8 feet (2.4 m) tall.

Flowers: very small, massed on a cylindrical head, each with a tubular corolla, lilac to lavender, with stiff bracts longer than the flowers; the heads subtended by long, up-curving linear bracts which normally exceed the height of the inflorescence; much reminiscent of thistle.

Leaves: opposite, joined around stem (at least the upper), lance-shaped, crenate, without spines except on midvein beneath.

A close relative, *D. fullonum,* was cultivated here and abroad, the dried flowerheads used on spindles to raise the nap of woolen cloth.

Dipsacus, Greek, "to thirst," referring to the water-storing ability of many species that have joined leaves, forming saucers; *sylvestris,* Latin, "of the woods," though our teasel is never found in wooded areas.

Heath Family *Ericaceae*

About 100 genera with 3,000 species of worldwide distribution. Includes *Rhododendron* with 1,200 species and heath (*Erica*) with 500 more. Mostly shrubs of acid soils in the Himalayas, New Guinea and southern Africa. For floral details see page 14. Of economic importance: blueberries and the culture of rhododendrons. Missouri has two genera *Rhododendron*—one species and *Vaccinium*—three species.

Rhododendron roseum (90) Azalea, Rhododendron, Honeysuckle
April–May

Habitat: north-facing slopes and along streams on acid soils in southeast and southwest Ozarks. Woody shrub to 7 feet (2.1 m) tall.

Flowers: in terminal racemes; long, tubular with 5 lobes, protruding stamens and pistil; pink, rose or rarely white, very fragrant.

Leaves: to 4" (10 cm) long, leathery, hairy underneath, oblong.

In nature, *R. roseum* grows in shade only, but it will do well even in full sun with a southern exposure under cultivation.

Native Ozarkians use the name honeysuckle exclusively.

Rhododendron, Greek, "red tree;" *roseum,* Latin, "rose-colored."

Vaccineum stamineum (35) Highbush Huckleberry, Deerberry
April–June

Habitat: acid soils of open woods; upland areas of the Ozarks. Shrub to 10 feet (3 m) tall, much-branched.
Flowers: small, bell-shaped, white, each with its stalk subtended by a bractlike small leaf near end of branches. Stamens protrude conspicuously; the green calyx is 5-pointed as is the corolla. Flowers hang downward.
Leaves: alternate, ovate, thinly hairy, to 3" (7.5 cm) long.
Fruit: berries are edible but not delectable.

> *Vaccineum,* the classical Latin name for blueberry; *stamineum,* Latin, "of stamens," because they protrude.

Vaccineum arboreum Farkleberry, Tree Huckleberry
July–Oct.

Habitat: distribution and appearance like *V. stamineum.*
Flowers: much later in season than *V. stamineum;* very similar except that stamens do NOT protrude.

> *arboreum,* Latin, "treelike."

Vaccineum pallidum (80) Lowbush Blueberry
April–May

Habitat: acid soils, open woods, upland forests in Ozarks and east-central Missouri. Low shrub, much-branched, to 20" (5 dm) tall; an indicator of acid soil.
Flowers: in clusters along stems, bell-shaped, hanging down, with a green calyx slightly longer than broad, greenish white.
Leaves: small, ovate with very fine teeth, not over 1½" (4 cm) long.
Fruit: edible, a bluish-black berry, sweet-sour, ripening a few at a time and never plentiful. Animals appreciate them.

> *pallidum,* Latin, "pale" (the little bell-flowers).

Spurge Family *Euphorbiaceae*

About 300 genera with 5,000 species, mainly tropical, but also Mediterranean, the U.S., and eastern and South Africa. The family developed in Africa into succulents in parallel evolution with the cacti of the Americas. Floral details vary widely. *Hevea brasiliensis,* para-rubber; manioc and cassava, tapioca; *Ricinus,* castor oil; *Vernicia* species, tung-oil. Poinsettia and croton are cultivated. Missouri has seven genera with 32 species.

Euphorbiaceae

Euphorbia: Of 20 species in Missouri, the 7 described below have a wide distribution. All contain a milky, acrid juice, poisonous to animals, causing rashes in humans. Euphorbias do not have flowers as normally envisioned, but have a cup (the cyathium) in which a number of staminate flowers are inserted. The ovary is on a stem which grows out of the cup after fertilization has taken place.

Euphorbia Key

1a) Stem erect—leaves alternate on stems
    2a) leaves edged white . . . . *marginata*
    2b) leaves and inflorescence green
        3a) upper leaves below umbel broadly triangular, nearly joined . . . . *commutata*
        3b) leaves of various shapes . . . . *heterophylla*
        3c) leaves blunt obtuse, to 1½" (4 cm) long . . . . *obtusata*
    2c) leaves green, inflorescence with white, petal-like appendages
    . . . . *corollata*
1b) Stem erect—leaves opposite
    2a) leaves narrow lanceolate, toothed . . . . *dentata*
    2b) leaves very short, blunt, to 1½" (35 mm) long . . . . *maculata*

Euphorbia marginata Snow-on-the-Mountain
June–Oct.

Habitat: native to loess hills of northwest Missouri, escaped from gardens in many places. Stems erect, soft and hairy.
Inflorescence: small, greenish, upright cups with stamens protruding in small terminal groups.
Leaves: sessile, broadly ovate, alternate. Leaves subtending the inflorescences with white margins.

> *Euphorbia,* for Euphorbus, the physician of King Juba of Mauritania; *marginata,* Latin, "with a margin."

Euphorbia obtusata Blunt-leaved Spurge
May–June

Habitat: low woods, fields, valleys; scattered in south, central and east-central counties. Simple stem with few lateral branches, usually about 2 feet (60 cm) tall.
Inflorescence: light green, terminal.
Leaves: bluntly obtuse, to 1½" (4 cm) long; very fine teeth, alternate.

> *obtusata,* Latin, "blunt" (the leaves).

Euphorbia commutata (79) Wood Spurge
April–June

Habitat: woods, valleys, streamsides, waste areas; central and eastern counties. Low, upright to 16" (4 dm) tall. A conspicuous plant of early spring due to the light green color.
Inflorescence: very small (see *Euphorbia* introduction for floral details).
Leaves: alternate along stem, sessile, short and rounded. Leaves below inflorescences rather large, in a whorl and rounded. Both types yellow-green.

commutata, Latin, "changing" (the leaf shapes, see above).

Euphorbia heterophylla Painted Leaf or Wild Poinsettia
July–Oct.

Habitat: fields, valleys, waste places, roadsides; statewide except Southeast Lowlands and some northern counties. Annual with branched stem, to 3 feet (90 cm) tall but normally lower.
Inflorescence: terminal in small groups, green (for details see *Euphorbia* introduction).
Leaves: in variable shapes even on the same plant, either ovate or lobed with pointed or rounded lobes. Upper leaves just below inflorescence often red or with red base.

heterophylla, Greek, "various-leaved."

Euphorbia corollata (46) Flowering Spurge
May–Oct.

Habitat: fields, glades, open woods, rocky places, roadsides, railroads; statewide. Often to 3 feet (90 cm) tall with a much-branched top.
Inflorescence: when growing on poor ground only a few, but in rich soils plants may spread as wide as they are tall with an abundance of inflorescences. The cups are white with white, petal-like appendages (see *Euphorbia* introduction for details).
Leaves: alternate on stems, sessile, narrowing toward base, ovate. Those at points of branching are in whorls. Leaves near inflorescences opposite.

corollata, Latin, "with a corolla."

Euphorbia dentata Toothed Spurge
July–Oct.

Habitat: fields, waste places, roadsides; statewide. About 16" (4 dm) tall, often branched.
Inflorescence: interspersed with many leaves.
Leaves: opposite on stems, hairy, with petioles, ovate, coarsely toothed.

dentata, Latin, "toothed."

Euphorbia maculata Nodding Spurge
May–Oct.

Habitat: fields, cultivated areas, waste places, roadsides; statewide. A low, erect plant, much-branched.
Inflorescence: tiny.
Leaves: opposite, oval, to 1½" (35 mm) long, folding late in day.

A common weed. Leaves often blotched.

maculata, Latin, "splotched."

Pea Family *Fabaceae (Leguminosae)*

About 700 genera and 17,000 species worldwide. For floral details see page 14. Of great importance to humans. *Crop Plants:* **clover, alfalfa, cowpeas and others, all symbiotic with nitrogen-fixing bacteria.** *Food Plants:* **peas, beans, lentils, chickpeas, soybeans, peanuts.** *Garden Plants:* **peas, lupines, wisteria.** *Trees:* **acacia, yellow wood, Kentucky coffeetree, locust, honeylocust, redbud, golden-rain tree, Chinese scholar tree. Excluding garden plants and doubtful railroad adventives, Missouri has 40 genera with 123 species, of which 27 are introduced.**

Note: All species of *Fabaceae* described here have the typical peaflower (see page 21), unless indicated in text.

Amorpha canescens (113) Lead Plant
May–Aug.

Habitat: fields, prairies, glades; statewide except Southeast Lowlands. A much-branched shrub, densely hairy, to 3 feet (90 cm) tall.
Flowers: tiny, massed in tight spikes; yellow stamens protruding from lavender flowers. The flowers reduced to the top petal (the "sail"), lacking the other petals (the "wings" and "keel.")
Leaves: compound, with up to 25 short, rounded, gray-hairy leaflets.

It is assumed that the name "lead plant" comes from the gray appearance.

Amorpha, Greek, "without shape" or "deformed," the simplified flowers; *canescens,* Latin, "gray hair."

Astragalus mexicanus (56) Ground Plum, Milk Vetch,
March–May   Buffalo Pea

Habitat: open woods, embankments, roadsides, glades, fields; counties adjacent and south of Missouri River. Many-stemmed, bushy plant to about 20" (5 dm) tall.
Flowers: in tight racemes nearly 1" (25 mm) long, cream-colored with lilac-blue tips of the keel petals.

Leaves: compound, with many opposite, oblanceolate leaflets.
Fruit: nearly ball-shaped with a central ridge which is pointed; smooth, about ¾" (2 cm) wide. Edible in unripe stage.

Astragalus, Greek, name of a member of the Pea Family; *mexicanus,* the species grows in Texas and may well have been reported originally from adjacent Mexico.

Astragalus mexicanus, fruit; actual size of pod 2".

Astragalus canadensis Rattle Weed
May–Aug.

Habitat: open, wet lowlands, rarely upland; statewide. Tall, upright, branched, to 4 feet (1.2 m) high.
Flowers: in long inflorescences; regular pea flower shape, greenish white to cream-colored.
Leaves: compound with many opposite leaflets that get shorter toward tip; oblong to elliptical.

Baptisia leucantha (44) Wild White Indigo
May–July

Habitat: prairies, fields, glades, roadsides, streamsides; statewide. Prefers moist areas, to 5 feet (1.5 m) tall or higher, branched perennial.
Flowers: pure white in erect or curved racemes, regular pea flower shape.
Leaves: all along stems, divided into 3 leaflets, narrow, oblong.

It is likely that *B. leucantha* is poisonous.

Baptisia, Greek, "to dye" as some *Baptisia* species provide coloring material; *leucantha,* Greek, "white-flowered."

Fabaceae

Baptisia leucophaea (59) Long-bracted Wild Indigo
April–June

Habitat: rocky, open woods, fields, often along roads, openings in woods, streamsides, usually on acid soil; statewide except Southeast Lowlands. Low, bushy, to 12" (30 cm) tall, the earliest flowering *Baptisia*.

Flowers: many pea-type flowers on a heavy, long raceme, drooping by its weight, cream-colored.

Leaves: with prominent bracts, divided into 3 leaflets, to 3" (7½ cm) long, oblanceolate.

leucophaea, Greek, "cream-colored."

Baptisia australis Blue False Indigo
May–June

Habitat: limestone glades, fields in south and east-central counties. Branched, to 3 feet (90 cm) tall but on glades usually much lower.

Flowers: pea-shaped, blue to violet on upright racemes.

Leaves: on short petioles, trifoliate.

The flowers have been used as a poor substitute for indigo in dying.

australis, Latin, "southern."

Cassia marilandica (77) Wild Senna
July–Aug.

Habitat: edges of woods, bases of slopes, open fields, thickets, generally in moist situations; statewide. From 3–8 feet (.9–2.4 m) tall, normally with 1 stem, perennial.

Flowers: in short racemes which arise on stems from the leaf axils, yellow. Flowers appear to be regular (not pea-shaped) and consist of 5 spreading petals of which 2 are larger than the other 3.

Leaves: compound with 4–8 pairs of oblong leaflets, to 2" (5 cm) long. Senna leaves have had medicinal use and as a cathartic.

Cassia, the Greek name of the cassia-bark tree, which Linnaeus applied to this genus.

Cassia fasciculata (73) Partridge Pea
June–Oct.

Habitat: fields, waste places, roadsides, railroads; statewide. One of the most commonly seen roadside plants of early fall, about 2 feet (6 dm) tall with upright stems.

Flowers: 1 to several, arise from leaf axils, nearly equal petals; yellow, sometimes with a touch of red-purple at base, about 1" (2½ cm) across. The *Cassias* belong to the subfamily *Caesalpinioideae* of the *Fabaceae*, their floral pattern being quite different from the pea flower shape.

Leaves: compound, pinnately divided, with up to 18 leaflets which are narrow, short, linear. Leaflets fold up along midrib upon touching.
Fruit: a short pod; the seeds are eaten by quail and many other birds.

fasciculata, Latin, "in bundles," the leaflets.

Cassia nictitans Sensitive Pea
July–Sept.

Habitat: fields, rocky woods, upland slopes; on acid soils mainly south of Missouri River. Small, spreading, hairy annual, to 12" (30 cm) in dry situations.
Flowers: yellow, small, arising from leaf axils; nearly equal petals.
Leaves: as for other cassias (above) but very small, the leaflets a little over ½" (15 mm) long.

nictitans, Latin, "winking," referring to the leaves closing and opening.

Cercis canadensis (87) Redbud, Judas Tree
March–May

Habitat: open woods, edges of woods, glades; statewide. Understory tree, usually small, but as an ornamental in cultivation it easily attains a diameter of 1 foot (30 cm) or more; wide spreading, with brittle branches.
Flowers: single or in small groups, emerge on stems directly from the branches, purple-red to pink-lavender, pea flower-shaped. Flowers appear before the leaves. A white form has been found only once in the wild and is now cultivated.
Leaves: heart-shaped on long stems. They change their position from horizontal to vertical during the heat of summer to minimize evaporation.
Fruit: the seedpods are numerous, 2-3" (5-8 cm) long; seeds are eaten by squirrels.

"Judas tree" from the legend that Judas hanged himself from a member of the genus. *Cercis,* Latin, the name of the oriental Judas tree.

Clitoria mariana (98) Butterfly Pea
May–Sept.

Habitat: acid soils in open upland or lowland woods, streamsides of southern Missouri. Low, shrublike, twisting branches (but not a climber).
Flowers: solitary or few on very short peduncles, pea flower-shaped, to 2" (5 cm) long, beautifully colored pale blue and lilac with darker veining, arising from leaf axils. One author postulates that late in the season the plant produces small, budlike, insignficant flowers, which also produce seed.

Fabaceae

Leaves: with 3 leaflets, the center on a longer stem than the lateral.
Fruit: a long pod about 2" (5 cm) long.

Clitoria, a reference to the resemblance of the flower to human anatomy; *Mariana,* Latin, "Mary."

Coronilla varia (96) Crown Vetch
May–Aug.

Habitat: fields, waste places, roadways; widely planted by Missouri Highway Department. Native of Europe, Asia and Africa. A creeping ground cover about 1 foot (30 cm) high.
Flowers: massed in umbels like a "crown"; typical pea flower-shaped, pink and white or all white.
Leaves: compound with up to 21 oblong leaflets.

Coronilla, Latin, "little crown"; *varia,* Latin, "diverse," (the floral colors).

Desmodium: Missouri has 18 species. Identification is difficult and often depends on analysis of the seedpods; it is beyond the scope of this presentation.

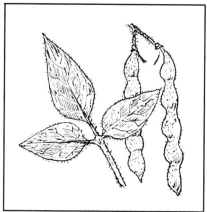

Desmodium canescens, fruit and leaf; actual length of fruit 5 cm.

Desmodium canescens (104) Tick-Trefoil, Beggar's Lice
July–Sept.

Habitat: open woods, valleys, shaded places; scattered statewide. Erect stem with a few prominent branches, hairy, 3 feet (9 dm) or taller.
Flowers: on long peduncles with several racemes, pale violet, pea flower-shaped.

Leaves: 3-divided on long petioles, hairy, ovate, the center leaflet on a long stem, the lateral on very short stems.

Fruit: in distinct papery pods which break up into 1-seeded segments that are dispersed by animals. The pods are hairy and stick to clothing and animals, therefore the name beggar's lice. The plants of this genus are important browse for deer, the seeds are sustenance for many birds.

Desmodium, Greek, "band" or "chain" (the seedpods); *canescens,* Latin, "gray-downy."

Lathyrus latifolius (92) Perennial Pea
May–Sept.

Habitat: fencerows, roadways, railroads, fields; scattered statewide. Strong climber, often covering large areas. Stems broadly winged. Native of Europe.

Flowers: in clustered inflorescences with up to 10 flowers, about 1" (2.5 cm) long, large standard, rose-purple, rose-pink, white, without any scent.

Leaves: their stems with lanceolate stipules; leaves in sets of 2 on a winged petiole, terminated by tendrils.

Lathyrus, Greek, the name of some legume; *latifolius,* Latin, "broad-leaved."

Lespedeza: There are 15 species found in Missouri, many difficult to identify in the field.

Lespedeza procumbens (103) Bush Clover
Aug.–Oct.

Habitat: acid soils on slopes and ridges; south of Missouri River and north of it in central and eastern Missouri. Stems trailing or lying on ground with short, upright, finely hairy branches.

Flowers: many near terminals of branches, tiny, typical pea flowers, light violet.

Leaves: elliptical to oval, to 2" (5 cm) long, mostly shorter; eaten by deer and turkey, and the fruits by turkey and quail.

Lespedeza, with an error in spelling, commemorates V.M. Cespedes, governor of Florida, 1784-1790; *procumbens,* Latin, "lying down."

Lespedeza virginica (95) Bush Clover
May–Sept.

Habitat: dry, open woods, fields, streamsides, roadsides, railroads; statewide except extreme northwest. Stems to 3 feet (9 dm) tall, usually unbranched, which curve under their own weight of foliage.

Fabaceae

Flowers: on very short peduncles arising from the leaf axils, in small clusters along middle and upper stem, small, pink, pea flower-shaped.
Leaves: profuse, 3-divided, narrow linear, short.
Fruit: pods; seeds are eaten by birds.

Lotus corniculatus (70) Bird's-foot Trefoil
May–Sept.

Habitat: fields, roadsides, waste places; scattered throughout state. Native of Europe, introduced by Highway Department. Perennial, many-branched; the branches lie on the ground but their ends ascend.
Flowers: in umbels, terminal, pea flower-shaped, golden yellow.
Leaves: compound, with 3 leaflets (a terminal and 2 opposite) some distance below. Two basal leaves are not part of the compound leaf but are stipules. All are variably oblong.
Fruit: the seeds form in slender, upright pods. *L. corniculatus* has a wide distribution on all continents; low-growing, it needs no mowing and is planted widely.

Lotus, a name used in antiquity for many genera, chosen by Linneaus for this clover; *corniculatus,* Latin, "little-horned" (the seedpods).

Medicago lupulina (67) Black Medick
March–Nov.

Habitat: fields, lawns, waste places, rights of way; statewide. Introduced from Eurasia. Prostrate, spreading, but also ascending to 20" (5 dm) tall.
Flowers: terminal, in rounded to elongated racemes, very small, yellow, pea flower-shaped.
Leaves: trifoliate, elliptical, to ¾" (2 cm) long.
Fruit: a tiny 1-seeded pod, almost black.

A nutritious legume not much planted in our area.

Medicago, Greek, the name of alfalfa which was believed to originate from Medea, of the Greek legend; *lupulina,* Latin, "hoplike" (the leaves). Black medick has probably nothing to do with medicine, but derives from the botanical name.

Melilotus officinalis (63) Yellow Sweet Clover, Yellow Melilot
May–Oct.

Habitat: fields, waste places, rights of way; statewide. Tall, rigid, branched, to 6 feet (1.8 m) tall. Native of Eurasia.
Flowers: in long racemes ascending from leaf axils with stipules, very small, pea flower-shaped, light yellow, with a pleasant fragrance. Flowers over long period.

Leaves: trifoliate, leaflets oval, rounded at top, finely toothed.

Highly drought resistant, planted for hay, pasture and green manure.

Melilotus, Greek, "honey-lotus"; *officinalis,* Latin, indicates a former medicinal use.

Melilotus albus White Sweet Clover
May–Oct.

In every respect corresponds to *M. officinalis,* but flowers are white.

albus, Latin, "white."

Petalostemon purpureum (100) Purple Prairie Clover
June–Sept.

Habitat: glades, rocky open woods, rights of way; statewide except Southeast Lowlands. One or few stems from a common base, generally about 2 feet (6 dm) tall.
Flowers: terminal, in tight, rounded to cylindrical inflorescences. Individual florets with only 1 petal, the other 4 that look like petals are very narrow and are really staminodes, false stamens; color rose-magenta to rose-purple. Buds covered by silvery hair. Flowers open in a circle around the "head" from the bottom upward.
Leaves: linear, 3- to 5-divided, the opposite leaflets spreading from the midrib with a terminal leaflet. Leaves subtended by extremely narrow bracts.

Petalostemon, Greek, "petal and stamen," the unusual union of these parts in this genus; *purpureum,* Latin, "purple."

Petalostemon candidum White Prairie Clover

All information identical to *P. purpureum,* but the flowers are white.

candidum, Latin, "white."

Psoralea Key (based on leaflets)

1a) 3 Leaflets
  2a) leaflets on long petioles, center leaflet on a much longer stalk . . . . *onobrychis*
  2b) leaflets on short petiole, center leaflet on a much longer stalk . . . . *psoralioides*
  2c) leaflets on short petiole, all on same length stalks (very short) . . . . *tenuiflora*
1b) 5 Leaflets . . . . *esculenta*

Fabaceae

Psoralea onobrychis (115) French Grass
May–Sept.

Habitat: wooded slopes, low open areas, river banks; valleys of eastern Missouri. Leafy, much-branched, to 2½ feet (75 cm) tall.
Flowers: loose, upright spikes, small, pale blue to purple to whitish, on long stems from leaf axils.
Leaves: on long stems, trifoliate, the middle leaflet on a longer stem. Leaflets ovate, pointed at both ends to 4" (10 cm) long and about half as wide.

Psoralea, Greek, "scurfy," referring to dots covering leaves and stems; *onobrychis,* Greek, means that the plant looks like an *Onobrychis,* another member of the Pea Family.

Psoralea psoralioides Sampson's Snakeroot
May–July

Habitat: open woods, rock outcroppings, on acid soils; south of Missouri River. Appearance like *P. onobrychis.*
Flowers: on very long peduncles, small, pea flower-shaped, blue.
Leaves: on short stems, trifoliate, with narrow, elliptical leaflets, the center one on a longer stem than the laterals.

psoralioides, Greek, "like a *Psoralea,*" the species formerly had another generic name.

Psoralea tenuiflora Scurfy Pea
May–Sept.

Habitat: limestone glades, fields, open woods; absent from Southeast Lowlands. Taller than other *Psoraleas,* to 4 feet (1.2 m).
Flowers: very small on spaced out inflorescences, purplish, pea flower-shaped.
Leaves: trifoliate, on petioles, rarely with 5 leaflets; leaflets narrow lanceolate, to 1½" (4 cm) long.

tenuiflora, Latin, "slender-flowered."

Psoralea esculenta Prairie Turnip, Wild Potato
April–July

Habitat: rocky fields, glades, open slopes; scattered south of Missouri River. To 18" (45 cm) tall, extremely hairy all over.
Flowers: almost covered by white hair, in dense spikes, blue-purple.
Leaves: 5-divided, palmate, to 4" (10 cm) long.

A relatively uncommon plant which needs protection from humans and grazing wherever found.

esculenta, Latin, "edible."

Robinia pseudoacacia (42) Black Locust (erroneously called *May-June* Honey Locust)

Habitat: upland woods, pastures, waste areas, streamsides; statewide. Large tree to 70 feet (21 m) tall.

Flowers: in long racemes, typical pea flower-shaped, white with a yellow splotch on the standard.

Leaves: compound with 7-19 oval leaflets, rounded at top and bottom, drooping and closing up in the evening.

Spines: small, stout, on young, fast-growing twigs only. (The honey locust, with its large, massed thorns is *Gleditsia triacanthos,* another member of the Pea Family).

Fruit: a pod to 4" (10 cm) long with 4-8 kidney-shaped seeds.

The tree is often badly damaged and killed by borers. The wood is rot-resistant and the strongest of any North American tree.

Robinia for Jean Robin (1550-1629), herbalist to Henry IV of France; *pseudoacacia,* "like an acacia."

Schrankia uncinata (98) Sensitive Brier
May-Sept.

Habitat: glades, fields, rights of way, waste places; statewide except northeast and Southeast Lowlands. A trailing or creeping plant of dry areas, entirely covered by hooked barbs.

Flowers: on long stalks arising from leaf axils in ball-shaped heads of many funnel-shaped pink to rose-colored florets with stamens protruding. This is a member of the subfamily *Mimosoideae* with floral design entirely different from the pea flower type.

Leaves: double compound with 13-15 leaflets, which are again divided into 8-16 tiny leaflets, called pinnules. These small leaflets can fold up and close like those of a mimosa.

Fruit: a very prickly pod to 3½" (9 cm) long.

Schrankia for Franz von Schrank, a German botanist of the 19th century; *uncinata,* Latin, "hooked" or "barbed."

Stylosanthes biflora (69) Pencil Flower
May-Sept.

Habitat: open woods, rock outcroppings, glades on acid soils; mainly south of Missouri River. Stems wiry, branched from base, sometimes trailing, low, usually not over 8" (20 cm) high.

Flowers: pea flower type with a large standard, the other petals much smaller; orange to orange-yellow, in small groups subtended by bracts.

Leaves: trifolate with partly joined bracts around petioles which are lanceolate to oblong, to 1½" (4 cm) long.

Fabaceae

Stylosanthes, Greek, "style-flower," probably because the style persists after the petals have fallen. The same explanation applies to the common name, "pencil flower." ***biflora***, Latin, "2-flowered" though there may be from 2–6 flowers in a spike.

Tephrosia virginiana (92) Goat's Rue, Hoary Pea
May–Aug.

Habitat: rocky, open woods, glades, fields, in acid soils; south of Missouri River, scattered north of it. Low, bushy, hairy plants, to 2 feet (60 cm) tall but usually shorter.

Flowers: in terminal racemes and others arising from leaf axils, with showy, pea flower type blossoms; the standards light yellow suffused with pink while the keel is pink or very pale purple.

Leaves: compound with normally 21 narrowly oblong leaflets.

Fruit: in small pods to 2" (5 cm) long.

Roots: contain rotenone, a deadly poison for fish and cold-blooded animals. Indians used the plant extract for fish-poison.

Tephrosia, Greek, "ash-colored" or "hoary," the appearance of the plant.

Vicia villosa (109) Hairy Vetch
April–Oct.

Habitat: fields, waste places, rights of way; scattered statewide. Native of Europe, much planted by Highway Department. Spreading, to 2½ feet (7.5 dm) high, forming a dense ground cover.

Flowers: in long racemes on long peduncles arising from leaf axils, with 10–30 flowers of the pea type all turned to one side of stalk, in varying colors: rich lavender, purple, violet or whitish.

Leaves: compound, ending in a tendril with 5–10 pairs of narrowly oblong leaflets.

Fruit: a small pod about 1" (½ cm) long.

Vicia, the classical Latin name for vetch; *villosa*, Latin, "long, soft, hairy."

Vicia caroliniana Wood Vetch
April–June

Habitat: rocky areas with acid soils in the Ozarks. Trailing or climbing. Very similar to *V. villosa* but the plant is smooth and hairless, and the flowers are white or whitish, the keel tipped with blue or lilac.

Fumitory Family *Fumariaceae*

Herbs of north temperate zone, a few in Africa, with 16 genera and about 400 species. Some authors combine the Fumitory Family with the Poppy Family. Flowers with two small sepals, which drop early in flowering, and four petals, usually of two unequal sizes, of which one or two are spurred, forming a cornucopia or heart-shaped flower. Missouri has two genera and seven species.

Corydalis flavula (57) Pale Corydalis
April–May

Habitat: rich woods, streamsides, below bluffs; south and central Missouri. All *Corydalis* species are delicate, low-growing, shade-loving forest dwellers, sometimes forming mats.

Flowers: in terminal racemes with a few florets, each light yellow, the petals converging (but not fused) into a tubelike appearance with a spur; the supporting stem attached near the center of the flower rather than the end.

Leaves: similar to Dutchman's breeches, compound with fernlike, dissected divisions, carried on flowering stems and arising from base, blue-green.

The 5 **Corydalis** species found in Missouri are all very much alike.

Corydalis, Greek, "crested lark," referring to the spurred flower; *flavula*, Latin, "yellowish."

Dicentra cucullaria (26) Dutchman's Breeches
March–May

Habitat: rich slopes of woods, bottomlands, streamsides; statewide except Southeast Lowlands. Low to about 1 foot (30 cm) tall. Demands excellent drainage and humus-rich soil.

Flowers: in terminal racemes on leafless stems (scapes), with 2 spurs (the "breeches") which diverge. Each flower is attached to a slender stem between 2 spurs. Flowers white, sometimes faint pink.

Leaves: on long petioles from base of plant, decompound (more than once divided), fernlike, blue-green.

Root: a cluster of grain-sized white tubers.

"Dutchman's Breeches" is a charming description of the floral shape. **Dicentra**, Greek, "2-spurred"; **cucullaria**, Latin, "hooded," as the tips of a pair of petals are joined over the inner part of the flower.

Dicentra canadensis Squirrel Corn
April–May

Habitat: moist, rich, low, wooded areas at base of north-facing or east-facing slopes; scattered in eastern Missouri. A fairly rare species, demanding as to suitable habitat. Differs from *D. cucullaria* by having the spurs rounded (and thus NOT having the "breeches" appearance).

Gentian Family *Gentianaceae*

Herbs, worldwide except North Africa, mostly in high altitudes and swamps. About 800 genera with 900 species. Leaves opposite or whorled. Flowers with bell-shaped corolla of four or five united sepals and petals. Stamens inserted in corolla alternate with lobes. Ovary superior. Missouri has six genera with 12 species, of which at least four were known from only one locality.

Gentiana andrewsii (118) Closed Gentian, Bottle Gentian
Aug.–Oct.

Habitat: low woods, streamsides, below bluffs, scattered through most of Missouri. Stems to 2½ feet (75 cm) long, either upright or trailing.
Flowers: in dense, terminal clusters, or a few from upper leaf axils, to 1½" (4 cm) long, always closed, cylindrical. Color changes from wine-red through purple to "gentian" blue. Long-flowering.
Leaves: large to 6" (15 cm) long, ovate-lanceolate, opposite, appearing whorled, dark green.

The flowers are visited by bumblebees who push their way into the flowers.
Gentiana, for King Gentius who is credited with discovering the medicinal value of some gentian species; *andrewsii* for the English botanist, Henry C. Andrews (1794–1830).

Sabatia angularis (99) Rose Gentian
June–Sept.

Habitat: glades, upland fields, margins of woods, roadsides, rights of way; in southern, northeastern and east-central counties. Biennial whose annual appearance is uncertain. To 2 feet (6 dm) tall with many opposite branches, giving it a candelabralike appearance; stems angled and square.
Flowers: on short and long peduncles from upper leaf axils, to 1" (2½ cm) across, 5 petal-like spreading lobes; pink, and in some localities white, with a green inner ring; delicate scent.
Leaves: opposite, sessile, ovate to lanceolate, to 1½" (4 cm) long.

Sabatia for Liberato Sabbati, an 18th century Italian botanist; *angularis,* Latin, "angular" (the stems).

Sabatia campestris Prairie Rose Gentian
July–Sept.

Habitat: prairies, fallow fields, roadsides; scattered in southern two-thirds of Missouri. Lower than *S. angularis,* to about 9" (23 cm) tall and in different habitat.
Flowers: the calyx lobes protruding between corolla lobes, which are pink.
Leaves: opposite, sessile, ovate-lanceolate, to 1½" (4 cm) long.

campestris, Latin, "of fields."

Swertia caroliniensis (81) American Columbo
May–June

(Also known as *Frasera caroliniensis.*)

Habitat: rich or rocky wooded slopes, valleys, streamsides in southeastern Missouri. Stiff, upright stalks to 8 feet (2.4 m) tall. Often in large colonies of basal leaf rosettes. The plant dies after flowering.
Flowers: in terminal, long panicles, whitish green, about 1" (2½ cm) across; 4 petal-like lobes with many purple dots, each lobe with a large gland surrounded by a fringe of fairly long hair.
Leaves: basal for several years prior to flowering; oblanceolate with a rounded end, sharply narrowing toward base, to 16" (4 dm) long. Leaves on flowering stalk in whorls, becoming progressively smaller toward the upper stalk. The withered stalks often remain standing during fall and the following winter, having shed the seeds.

Swertia, for Emanual Sweert, a 16th century Dutch horticulturalist.

Swertia caroliniensis, flower detail; actual size 1".

Geranium Family *Geraniaceae*

Mostly herbs and shrubs of 11 genera with about 750 species, mainly in temperate and subtropical zones. Leaves mostly deeply cleft. Flowers 5-merous, with brightly colored petals and 5–10 (rarely 15) stamens. The style persists and becomes the "crane's bill," the joined styles of five carpels. Cultivated geraniums belong to the genus *Pelargonium* of South African origin. Missouri has two genera: *Geranium* with two species and the introduced *Erodium* with one species.

Geranium maculatum (89) Wild Geranium, Crane's Bill
April–June

Habitat: open woods, borders of woods, shaded areas; statewide except Southeast Lowlands. Much-branched on stiff stems, to about 2 feet (6 dm) tall. Frequently found in colonies.
Flowers: few to several on long peduncles subtended by leaflike bracts, with 5 petals, 1" (2½ cm) across, deep magenta to pink or rose, the petals pencilled in darker shades. The 10 anthers wither before the stigma is receptive, ensuring cross-fertilization.
Leaves: long petioles, the basal 5–7 cleft into wedge-shaped sections, stem leaves only 2 on a stem, on shorter petioles and smaller.
Fruit: forms the sharply pointed "crane's bill."

Geranium, Greek, "crane" or "heron"; *maculatum*, Latin "spotted," the leaves are supposed to be but usually are not.

Geranium carolinianum Carolina Crane's Bill
May–July

Habitat: waste places, fields, rights of way; statewide. Much-branched, to 2 feet (6 dm) high.
Flowers: small, 5-petaled, pink, about ½" (12 mm) across.
Leaves: deeply cleft into 3–5 lobes, the lobes again much lobed.

Horse Chestnut Family *Hippocastanaceae*

A very small family of 2 genera with 15 species. Only one, *Aesculus*, is found in North America, the others in tropical Central America. Leaves palmate, inflorescence in showy racemes. Flowers irregular, 5-merous in our species. Winter buds are large with resinous scales. Fruit large, covered by a leathery capsule. There are two species in Missouri.

Aesculus glabra (60) Ohio Buckeye
April–May

Habitat: woods, valleys, below bluffs; throughout state except Southeast Lowlands. Understory tree, though rarely to 75 feet (23 m) tall.
Flowers: massed in upright racemes, usually 6–7" (15–18 cm) long. Individual flowers with 4 petals, greenish yellow, with 5–8 protruding stamens.
Leaves: palmately compound with 7 large leaflets, obovate, sharply pointed, to 6" (15 cm) long.
Fruit: a shiny brown nut in a leathery, soft-spiny capsule, relished by many wild animals.
Bark: furrowed, scaly, gray. The fruit is poisonous to humans.

Aesculus, Latin, the name of some mast-bearing tree; *glabra,* Latin, "smooth" or "without hair."

Aesculus pavia Red Buckeye
April–June

Habitat: bottomlands and swampy areas of southeastern Missouri. A slow-growing large shrub or small tree.
Flowers: as for *A. glabra* but red in color, rarely yellow.
Leaves: compound, palmate, with 5 leaflets; otherwise as *A. glabra.* *A. pavia* seems to prefer shade and is a good garden subject.

pavia, the former genus name of the species, for Peter Paaw of Leyden, Holland, who died in 1617.

Waterleaf Family *Hydrophyllaceae*

About 18 genera and 250 species of herbs in temperate and tropical zones, mainly in the Americas, absent from Eurasia. Leaves often splotched as if stained by raindrops, "waterleaf." Flowers usually blue or purple, five free sepals and five fused petals, ovary superior. Several species are used in horticulture. Missouri has four genera with 11 species.

Hydrophyllum appendiculatum (88) Woolen Breeches
April–July

Habitat: rich woods on slopes or in valleys; statewide except in southwest counties. Much-branched, to 2 feet (6 dm) tall, very hairy throughout.
Flowers: in loose groups (cymes), shallow lobed, light blue with purple-tipped stamens protruding slightly, usually borne above the leaves.
Leaves: thin, soft hairs, palmately 5-lobed, irregular, with coarse teeth on long petioles.

Hydrophyllaceae

Hydrophyllum, Greek, "waterleaf" (see family description above); *appendiculatum*, Latin, "with appendages," because the sepals have tiny reflexed appendages between them.

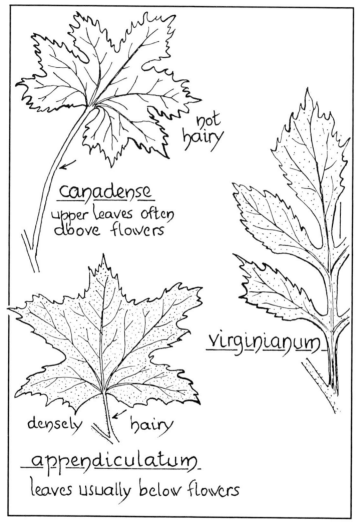

Hydrophyllum leaves

Hydrophyllum, Greek, "waterleaf" (see family description above); *appendiculatum,* Latin, "with appendages," because the sepals have tiny reflexed appendages between them.

Hydrophyllum virginianum Waterleaf
April–July

Habitat and Flowers: same as for *H. appendiculatum.*
Leaves: pinnately lobed (like a feather) with usually 5 segments and very coarse, large teeth (see drawing). This is a smooth species in contrast to the above.

Hydrophyllum canadense Canada Waterleaf
May–July

Habitat: moist, wooded areas of eastern and east-central Missouri.
Flowers: as for *H. appendiculatum* but usually borne BELOW the leaves.
Leaves: palmate on long petioles, with shallow lobing terminating in a few sharp points (see drawing).

Phacelia purshii (111) Phacelia, Miami Mist
April–June

Habitat: wooded lowlands, streamsides, moist rights of way, waste places; in east-central and southeast Missouri. Delicate plants, much-branched with slender stems, spreading, 12–18" (30–45 cm) tall.
Flowers: in loose, somewhat coiled cymes, 5-lobed, the lobes minutely fringed, light blue-violet or whitish; a large white "eye" with tiny dots in the center.
Leaves: to 3" (8 cm) long, deeply lobed, the lobes opposite; lower leaves petioled, upper leaves sessile. Leaf stems and stems in general with soft hairs.

Phacelia, Greek, "cluster" (the flowers); *purshii* for the German botanist Frederick Traugott Pursch (1774–1820) who claimed discovery of the species.

Phacelia gilioides Small-Flowered Phacelia
April–June

Habitat: quite variable on open ground south of Missouri River. Similar to *P. purshii* but flowers are NOT fringed.

gilioides, Greek, "like a gilia" (of the Phlox Family).

Phacelia hirsuta Hairy Phacelia
April–June

Habitat: and details as for *P. gilioides* but a stouter and larger plant with hairy stems and leaves.

hirsuta, Latin, "hairy."

St. John's-wort Family *Hypericaceae*

About 40 genera and 1,000 species of trees, shrubs and herbs; cosmopolitan, though centered in tropics. Leaves simple, usually opposite, covered with black dots or pits. Flowers mainly yellow, in cymes, 4- or 5-merous with many stamens, often united by their filaments. Many valuable species for timber, drugs, dyes, pigments and resins. Missouri has two genera: *Ascyrum* (St. Andrew's cross) with one species, and *Hypericum* (St. John's-wort) with 13. Some authors treat the *Hypericaceae* as a subfamily of the *Guttiferae* (Garciana Family) or the *Clusiaceae*.

Ascyrum hypericoides (67) St. Andrew's Cross
July–Oct.

Habitat: dry, open woods and cut-over woodlands; south of the Missouri River. Low shrub, much-branched; slightly woody stems and branches, to 10" (25 cm) tall. Missouri is its northernmost habitat.

Flowers: bright lemon-yellow; 4 petals form an oblique cross (the St. Andrew's cross); 4 sepals, of which 2 are large and 2 extremely small; many stamens, a characteristic of the family.

Leaves: opposite, sessile, lighter green below, narrowly oblong to 1" (2½ cm) long.

Ascyrum, Greek, "not rough," possibly an ancient name for some member of the family; *hypericoides,* Greek, "like a hypericon," the other genus in Missouri.

Hypericum Key

1a) Herbaceous plants
    2a) leaves reduced to scales or linear awl shape
        1) leaves awl-shaped, very short . . . . *drummondii*
        2) leaves reduced to scales . . . . *gentianoides*
    2b) leaves broader with nerves on either side of midrib
        1) few dots on petals, few or none on sepals . . . *perfoliatum*
        2) many dots on sepals AND petals . . . . *punctatum*
    2c) leaves with midrib only (no side nerves) . . . . *sphaerocarpum*
1b) Shrub with woody branches . . . . *spathulatum*

Hypericum drummondii Nits-and-Lice
June–Sept.

Habitat: acid soils on rock outcroppings in Ozarks; bushy-branched, to about 1 foot (3 dm) tall.

Flowers: in upper leaf axils, minute, 5-petaled, mostly solitary, yellow.

Leaves: linear, only ½" (15 mm) long, awl-shaped to adapt to severe climate.

Hypericum, Greek, of obscure meaning; *drummondii* for James Drummond, British naturalist in the 19th century.

Hypericum gentianoides Pine-Weed
July-Oct.

Habitat: acid soils and rock outcroppings in Ozarks. Much-branched, shrublike, not over 1 foot (1 dm) tall, usually lower. Very similar to *H. drummondii* but leaves are appressed (hugging the stems) and reduced; scalelike to avoid evaporation in an adverse habitat.

gentianoides, Greek, "like a gentian."

Hypericum punctatum Dotted St. John's-Wort
June-Sept.

Habitat: waste places, fallow fields, roadsides; statewide. To 3 feet (9 dm) tall from a woody base, with few branches below inflorescence.

Flowers: in a small, crowded inflorescence, 5-merous with many stamens, yellow. Both sepals and petals are heavily covered with black dots.

Leaves: oblong to ovate, rounded at tips, the larger 1-1½" (4-6 cm) long, opposite.

punctatum, Latin, "with dots."

Hypericum perforatum (69) Common St. John's-Wort
May-Sept.

Habitat: fields, waste places, roadsides, railroads; scattered statewide. Native of Europe. Shrublike, much-branched with leafy shoots, to 3 feet (9 dm) tall.

Flowers: many, in flat or domed inflorescences. Petals 5, broad at base with few black dots; sepals with or without a few black dots.

Leaves: many, crowded, opposite; at right angles with those above and below (decussate) *with many translucent spots*; sessile, linear to oblong, to 1½" (4 cm) long.

perforatum, Latin, "with perforations" (the leaves).

Hypericum mutilum Dwarf St. John's-Wort
July-Oct.

Habitat: wet, open places; scattered statewide except northern counties. Low, much-branched above the middle, about 1-2 feet (3-6 dm) tall.

Flowers: many, small, in much-branched inflorescences, the peduncles subtended by bracts, only about ¼" (4 mm) across, yellow with many stamens.

Leaves: sessile, opposite, 3-5 nerved, lanceolate to ovate; to 1¼" (3½ cm) long.

mutilum, Latin, "mutilated," because the specimen sent to Linneaus arrived in bad shape.

Hypericum sphaerocarpum Round-Podded St. John's-Wort
May–Sept.

Habitat: mainly in moist places, fields, open woods, gravel bars, low-lands; statewide. Stems erect, usually branched to 2½ feet (75 cm) tall.
Flowers: in generally compact inflorescences, yellow to orange, typical *Hypericum* flowers.
Leaves: with midrib only (no side nerves), opposite, linear to oblong, to 3" (7 cm) long.

sphaerocarpum, Greek, "round-seeded."

Hypericum spathulatum (72) Shrubby St. John's-Wort
June–Sept.

Habitat: dry or moist areas, wooded slopes, fallow fields, gravel bars; absent from northwest third of state. Densely branched, woody shrub, to 6 feet (1.8 m) tall, the twigs sharply 2-edged.
Flowers: in small groups (cymes), showy, 5-pointed with abundant stamens, yellow.
Leaves: opposite, narrow elliptical, abruptly narrowed toward base, to 2½" (6 cm) long, sessile, shiny, somewhat leathery.

spathulatum, Latin, "spatulalike," the shape of leaves.

Mint Family *Lamiaceae (Labiatae)*

A cosmopolitan family with about 200 genera and 3,000 species. For floral details, see page 14. Important herbs: catnip, marjoram, oregano, sage, thyme, lavender. Coleus and salvia are in horticultural use. Missouri has 27 genera with 57 species, of which 13 are introduced.

Blephilia ciliata (97) Ohio Horsemint
May–Aug.

Habitat: rich open woods, valleys and ravines, borders of woods; absent from western third of state. Usually unbranched with square and finely hairy stems, to 3 feet (9 dm) tall.
Flowers: in clusters toward end of stems which arise from nodes, with oval, pointed bracts and hairy fringes. Flowers have an upper and a 3-lobed lower lip, asymmetrical, typical of the Mint Family; pale lavender with purple spots.
Leaves: soft, opposite, lanceolate to ovate with only a few soft teeth, usually sessile. All green parts have a pleasant, mintlike scent. Basal leaves remain green all through the winter.

Blephilia, Greek, "eye-lashes," the soft hairy fringes of the bracts; *ciliata,* Latin, "soft hairy," also for the bracts.

Blephilia hirsuta Wood Mint
May–Sept.

Habitat: cool places, ravines, wooded slopes; scattered statewide. Very similar to *B. ciliata* but *B. hirsuta* is usually branched, the leaves have petioles and many fine teeth, and long, spreading hair.

hirsuta, Latin, "rough hairy."

Cunila origanoides (103) Dittany
July–Nov.

Habitat: acid soils on wooded slopes, borders of woods, shaded rights of way; in south, central and east-central counties. Low, much-branched, wiry, shrublike with square stems, to about 1 foot (3 dm).
Flowers: small, in tufts arising from leaf axils, purplish to lavender, each flower with a tiny, 2-lobed upper and a broader 3-lobed lower lip.
Leaves: opposite, sessile, almost triangular with a broad base and a lancelike point, finely toothed. The green parts have a delightful fragrance.

Cunila is one of few plants that form "frost-flowers." With the first severe freezes of a winter, water in the roots and stems is squeezed out of cracks in the stems, forming ribbonlike ice of amazing structures, the bands about 2" (5 cm) wide in elegant bows.

Cunila, an old Latin name for mint; *origanoides*, Greek, "like an oregano," a culinary herb.

Lamium amplexicaule (87) Henbit
Feb.–Nov.

Habitat: waste places, fields, gardens, roadsides, railroads; mostly south of Missouri River. Branching, soft, weedy plant with square stem, lacks a pleasant scent, to 10" (25 cm) tall. Native of Eurasia and Africa.
Flowers: in terminal clusters, subtended by sessile leaves, typical of Mint Family appearance, bright lavender with red spots.
Leaves: all but those subtending the inflorescence with stems, round, close to ground, becoming more elongate farther up the stem, bluntly toothed.

Lamium, Greek, "throat," the shape of the flower; *amplexicaule*, Latin, "around the stem," the appearance of the upmost leaves.

Lamium purpureum (88) Dead Nettle
April–Oct.

Habitat: waste places, gardens, roadsides, railroads; common south of Missouri River, scattered north of it. Much-branched weed, to about 10" (25 cm) tall, square stems, lacks a pleasant scent.

Lamiaceae

Flowers: in clusters above a dense canopy of massed leaves, dull rose-purple, with the typical Mint Family lips. A white form is fairly rare.

Leaves: on long petioles, those subtending the inflorescence on short stems, heart-shaped, bluish green, wrinkled, with scalloped margins.

purpureum, Latin, "purple."

Monarda russeliana (90) Horsemint, Wild Bergamot
April–June

Habitat: dry, open woods, glades, usually on acid soil; Ozarks and northeast counties. Square, unbranched stems, to about 3½ feet (1 m) tall.

Flowers: normally in 1 terminal cluster, subtended by many small leaves which frequently have rose-purple color. Floral tubes to 1½" (4 cm) long ending in 2 lips, the lower broad and recurving, the upper arching upward with stamens protruding. Color either whitish with purple spots or pale lavender.

Leaves: minutely hairy, inconspicuously toothed, lanceolate, opposite, nearly sessile, each pair at right angles to the nearest set. All parts of the plant have a pleasant aroma. The flowers attract butterflies.

Monarda, for the 16th century Spanish physician and herbalist Monardes; *russeliana* for Alexander Russel, a British physician of the 19th century.

Monarda fistulosa Wild Bergamot
May–Aug.

Habitat: fields, borders of woods, roadsides; variable statewide. Much-branched, pleasantly scented, to 3 feet (9 dm) tall, prominent in summer.

Flowers: as for *M. russeliana,* lavender, lilac or rose. The subtending bract-leaves pale green or tinged lilac.

Leaves: on definitive stalks, gray-green, fine hairs, ovate-lanceolate with small teeth.

fistulosa, Latin, "hollow" or "cylindrical," a supposed reference to the floral tube.

Perilla frutescens (105) Beef-Stake Plant
Aug.–Oct.

Habitat: moist or dry wooded bottomlands or open valley pastures; south of Missouri River, except north of it in a few eastern counties. Native of India. Annual, branched herb to 3 feet (1 m) tall, usually much lower.

Flowers: small, white or purple, in spikelike cymes arising from leaf axils in peduncles with small, bractlike leaflets. The 5 floral lobes well rounded.

Leaves: on long stems, large, soft, ovate to oblong, coarsely toothed, either green or shades of purplish-brown, highly aromatic.

Plant introduced as ornamental, widely naturalized. Seeds and leaves eaten in Japan. Seeds contain an edible oil which is also used as a cheap lacquer.

Perilla, the East Indian name of the species; *frutescens,* Latin, "shrubby, bushy", the appearance of the herb.

Physostegia virginiana (97) False Dragonhead, Obedient Plant
May–Sept.

(The genus is also known as *Dracocephalum*).

Habitat: moist places, fields, streamsides, lakesides; statewide. Single or sparingly branched stems, to 4 feet (1.2 m) tall.
Flowers: in long, terminal and a few lateral spikes, tightly spaced in vertical rows, pink to pale lilac, funnel-shaped with a hoodlike upper and a 3-divided lower lip.
Leaves: opposite, narrow lanceolate, sharply toothed, to 5" (13 cm) long.

There are 3 other *Physostegia* species in Missouri, all very similar to the above with a much more restricted distribution.

The name "obedient plant" because if flowers are pushed from their normal position they remain for some time where they have been turned.

Physostegia, Greek, "bladder-cover," the shape of the fruit.

Prunella vulgaris (114) Self-Heal, Heal-All
May–Sept.

Habitat: waste places, fields, along roads and railroads; statewide. Native of Europe. Generally about 1 foot (30 cm) tall with simple or branched, squared stems, sometimes creeping.
Flowers: in cylindrical spikes, blue, lavender or violet, the upper lip hooded, covering the stamens. Flowers are subtended by tiny, leaflike bracts.
Leaves: egg-lanceolate on petioles, opposite, to 4" (8 cm) long with wavy margins.

Prunella was originally Brunella of unknown meaning; *vulgaris,* Latin, "common."

Pycnanthemum tenuifolium (50) Slender Mountain Mint
June–Sept.

Habitat: dry, open woods, fields, roadsides, streamsides; statewide. Much-branched, to 2½ feet (75 cm) tall, square stemmed.

Lamiaceae

Flowers: in dense, half-round heads, minute, whitish, with long, nearly linear bracts below heads and very short bracts subtending the flowers. Upper lip not lobed, the lower with 3 distinct lobes. Sometimes the whitish flowers become a very light lavender.
Leaves: many, opposite, linear, commonly about 1½–2" (4-6 cm) long.

All parts of the species have a strong mint scent, and, as some would have it, a sage odor.

Pycnanthemum, Greek, "dense blossoms"; *tenuifolium,* Latin, "slender-leaved."

Pycnanthemum pilosum Hairy Mountain Mint
June–Sept.
All information same as for *P. tenuifolium* but the species is quite hairy and the leaves are somewhat wider, with hair on the underside.

pilosum, Latin, "soft hairy."

Scutellaria Key

1a) Plants 2½–3 feet tall, flowers in terminal racemes
   2a) leaves ovate-lanceolate, rounded at base . . . . *incana*
   2b) leaves ovate with heart-shaped base . . . . *ovata*
1b) Plants 2½–3 feet tall, flowers NOT in racemes but 2 or 3 arising
   from leaf axils . . . . *lateriflora*
1c) Plants to 1 foot tall . . . . *parvula*

Scutellaria: of 9 species found in Missouri, 4 occur widely.

Scutellaria incana (116) Skullcap
June–Sept.

Habitat: rocky, open woods, wooded slopes, streamsides in the Ozarks and north-central counties. Stems with closely pressed-on hair, branched, 2½–3 feet (75 cm–1 m) tall.
Flowers: in several terminal or near terminal racemes, purplish blue. The arching upper lip is the "scullcap," the lower lip flat, 3-lobed.
Leaves: opposite, to 6" (15 cm) long, the largest toward center of stalk, ovate-lanceolate with rounded base and coarse, blunted teeth, covered by fine hair. According to some, it is the seed which looks like a cap.

Scutellaria, Latin, "small dish," alluding to an appendage of the fruiting calyx; *incana,* Latin, "hoary," the leaves.

Scutellaria ovata Heart-Leaved Skullcap
May–Oct.

Habitat: open woods, glades, bluffs; absent from northern counties. Stout, erect stalk, 2½–3 feet (75 cm–1 m) tall, conspicuous soft hairs.

Flowers: in terminal racemes like *S. incana.*
Leaves: on long petioles with heart-shaped or rounded base and leaf tissue continuing into leaf stem, with rounded teeth.

ovate, Latin, "oval," the leaves.

Scutellaria lateriflora Mad-Dog Skullcap
June–Oct.

Habitat: only in wet places, low woods, river bottoms, streamsides, wet meadows; statewide. Stems usually branched, to 2½ feet (75 cm) tall.
Flowers: NOT in racemes, but single or up to 3 in upper leaf axils. Flower detail as in *S. incana.*
Leaves: on long petioles, the upper deltoid (triangular), the lower more ovate, all with dull, rounded teeth.

lateriflora, Latin, "sideways-flowered."

Scutellaria parvula Small Skullcap
May–July

Habitat: in dry fields, glades, ridges, uplands; statewide. Erect, hairy stems to 1 foot (3 dm) tall.
Flowers: in axils of upper stem leaves, usually just one. For floral detail see *S. incana.*
Leaves: opposite, sessile, ovate-lanceolate, small to ¾" (2 cm) long, often shorter.

parvula, Latin, "very small."

Teucrium canadense (101) Germander
June–Sept.

Habitat: fields, prairies, low woods, streamsides, roadsides, railroads; statewide. Stem rarely branched, to 3 feet (9 dm) tall.
Flowers: in terminal and lateral racemes, densely spaced, the small, 4-lobed upper lobes turned forward, *so that there seems to be no upper lip,* the lower lip being much larger; 4 stamens protrude on the sides of the corolla, color lavender or pink.
Leaves: opposite, lanceolate, sharply pointed; on petioles, with sharp or rounded teeth.

Teucrium, for Teucer, the first king of Troy, who may have used a European species medicinally.

Laurel Family *Lauraceae*

Mainly tropical and subtropical trees and shrubs of about 92 genera and 2,500 species; most of them produce aromatic oils. Flowers 3-merous, sepals and petals look alike. Many trees furnish valuable wood; *Cinnamonum* source of cinnamon and camphor; *Persea americana* is the avocado; bay laurel provides aromatic leaves, and sassafras an aromatic oil. Laurel and spicebush are ornamentals. Missouri has two genera with three species.

Lindera benzoin (55) Spice Bush
March–May

Habitat: low, moist woods, streamsides, bottomlands; south of Missouri River and east-central counties. Much-branched shrubs with smooth branches, to about 10 feet (3 m) in our climate.

Flowers: in yellow greenish clusters on stems arising from last year's leaf nodes before leaves appear. Most shrubs are dioecious, having "male" and "female" flowers on separate shrubs.

Leaves: alternate, on petioles, thick, obovate narrowed toward base, to 1 foot (3 dm) long.

Fruit: brilliant red ellipsoid drupe. The shrub spreads through root runners. All plant parts are strongly, pleasantly aromatic, the oil having been used extensively in medical and toilet preparations.

Lindera, for Johann Linder (1676–1723) a Swedish botanist; *benzoin,* Arabic or Semitic for "a gum or perfume."

Sassafras albidum, fruit and leaf; actual size of leaf 6".

Sassafras albidum (55) Sassafras
April–May

Habitat: dry, acid soils, borders of woods, ridges, fields, fencerows, valleys; south of Missouri River and east-central counties. Mostly seen as a small tree but can attain height of 60 feet (18 m) or more. Forms colonies through root suckers.

Flowers: in small groups on stems arising from last year's leaf terminal; greenish yellow, "male" and "female" flowers on separate trees.

Leaves: on long petioles, variable on same tree, ovate and entire or 2- or 3-lobed with irregular lobes, often mittenlike, narrowing toward base, to 7" (18 cm) long. Fall color a brilliant yellow. Leaves and twigs pleasantly aromatic.

Bark: deeply furrowed, a beautiful red-brown.

Fruit: blue-black drupes (stone fruit with a soft envelope) on long, red peduncles.

Sassafras, believed to be an adaptation of the Spanish *salsafras,* the common name given the tree by early French settlers; *albidum,* Latin, "white," or "whitish," referring to the "bloom" on buds and young branches. In the 18th century untold shiploads of sassafras were transported to Europe because of the belief that extracts were remedial for venereal disease.

Loosestrife Family *Lythraceae*

About 22 genera and 450 species of tropical and temperate zones, mainly of wet habitats. Flowers usually regular with four or six sepals and petals with twice as many stamens, the latter often of varying length (heterostyly). Leaves opposite or in whorls. *Lawsonia inermis* furnishes henna dye; crepe myrtle (*Lagerstroemia*) and loosestrife (*Lythrum*) are ornamentals. Missouri has six genera and eight species. Many species called "loosestrife" belong in the Primrose Family.

Lythrum alatum (99) Winged Loosestrife
June–Sept.

Habitat: in wet places, fields, swamps, ditches, margins of ponds and sloughs; statewide. Smooth, erect perennial with squared stems and rigid branches, to 3 feet (9 dm) tall.

Flowers: arising singly from upper leaf axils, deep magenta, 6-petaled, dimorphic (in a flower, either the stamens are longer than the pistil or the reverse).

Leaves: linear-oblong to lanceolate, mostly opposite with some of the upper alternate; progressively smaller toward top of plant.

Lythrum, Greek, "clotted blood" for a European species; *alatum,* Latin, "winged," because the stems have marginal angles. Loosestrife is a mistranslation of the Greek *Lysimachia.*

A close relative, *Lythrum salicaria* (from Eurasia) has a bad tendency to spread in wetlands, supplanting and eliminating native flora. But cultivars of this species, sold under many names by nurseries, are sterile and make useful garden subjects. If *Lythrum salicaria* threatens to take over your wetland habitat, a flyer titled "Stop Purple Loosestrife" can be obtained from the Department of Conservation.

Mallow Family *Malvaceae*

About 80 genera with 1,000 species, centered in South America; cosmopolitan. The genus *Hibiscus* accounts for 300 species. For floral details, see page 12. Economically most important is *Gossypium*, cotton. Okra is a *Hibiscus*. Horticultural subjects: mallows, hollyhocks, hibiscus. Excluding rarely escaped garden plants, Missouri has four genera with 12 species, three of them introduced.

Hibiscus lasiocarpos (102) Rose Mallow
July–Oct.

Habitat: borders of lakes, sloughs, swamps, in ditches, wet lowlands; eastern, southern and southeast Missouri. Tall, perennial herbs, sometimes with woody stalks to 8 feet (2.4 m) tall.

Flowers: One of the largest wildflowers in Missouri, about 6" (16 cm) across, 5 petals, and many protruding stamens united around the style, with a spreading head, white or rose with a central wine-purple spot.

Leaves: large, somewhat heart-shaped, rarely lobed; dense, fine hairs on upper side.

Seeds: eaten by ducks and quail.

Hibiscus, the Greek name of some species of the Mallow Family; *lasiocarpos,* Greek, "rough-fruited," the large, hard seed capsule.

Hibiscus militaris Halberd Leaf, Rose Mallow
July–Oct.

Habitat and description as for *H. lasiocarpos* but leaves are shaped like an ancient halberd lance with a central and 2 lateral sharp points.

militaris, Latin, "soldierlike."

Sida spinosa (75) Prickly Sida, Prickly Mallow
June–Oct.

Habitat: fields, waste places, roadsides, railroads; statewide. Native of New and Old World tropics. Small, much-branched, to 18" (45 cm) tall.

Flowers: in leaf axils of upper stems, with 5 petals, yellow to orange-yellow, the stamens joined around the pistil (a feature of mallows); about 1/3" (8 mm) across.

Leaves: on long stems, ovate to oblong with crenate margins. Leaf stems have at their base a small, spinelike projection which is NOT a spine and quite soft.

Sida, an old Greek name chosen by Linnaeus; *spinosa,* Latin, "spiny," see above.

Four-o'clock Family *Nyctaginaceae*

About 30 genera and 290 species, mostly tropical, a few North American. Flowers lack petals, while sepals act like them, surrounded by calyxlike bracts, tubular with five lobes, five stamens in alternate position with the lobes. Ovary superior. Ornamentals: bougainvillea, four-o'clock (*Mirabilis jalapa*). Missouri has one genus with four native species.

Mirabilis nyctaginea (93) Four-o'clock
May–Oct.

Habitat: fields, waste places, roadways, railroads; statewide. Smooth stems, branched above, to 2½ feet (75 cm) tall.

Flowers: in many-flowered terminal panicles, minute, arising from a green, 5-lobed involucre, light pink to purplish.

Leaves: on petioles, except a few of the uppermost (the only *Mirabilis* in Missouri with petioles), triangular (deltoid) or heart-shaped, to 3½" (9 cm) long, opposite.

"Four-o'clock" because the flowers open in the afternoon. *Mirabilis,* Latin, "strange" or "wonderful," probably the late opening of the flowers; *nyctaginea,* Greek, resembling a *Nyctago,* a member of the family.

Mirabilis albida Pale Umbrella Wort
May–Oct.

Habitat: bluffs, glades, fields, open land; statewide except northeast counties. Similar to *M. nyctaginea,* but flowers are white-lilac to pinkish and leaves are opposite, sessile, narrow lanceolate.

albida, Latin, "whitish."

Waterlily Family *Nymphaeaceae*

Worldwide except in cold climates, 9 genera with about 90 species, in fresh water. Usually with large leaves either floating or above water, each on its own stalk. Flowers with indefinite petals and stamens and a large ovary either superior or inferior; extensively cultivated. *Cabomba*, rare in Missouri, is an oxygenator in aquaria. Missouri has five genera with one species each, three of them quite rare.

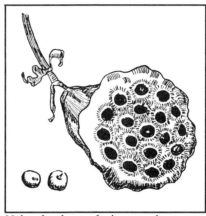

Nelumbo lutea, fruit; actual diameter 4".

Nelumbo lutea (73) American Lotus
June–Sept.

(Some authors put members of the genus *Nelumbo* into a separate family, the *Nelumbonaceae* (Lotus Family).)

Habitat: oxbow lakes, sloughs, ponds; scattered statewide. In still water with mud bottom *Nelumbo* will cover large areas.

Flowers: held singly above water; 20 or more sepals and petals, light yellow, to 8" (20 cm) across, with a central elevated receptacle of the ovary.

Leaves: normally above water level, circular, extremely variable in size, to 2 feet (6 dm) in diameter. They shed water.

Fruit: the receptacle, to 5" (13 cm) wide, becomes woody as the seeds ripen. Seeds acornlike anchored in deep pits.

American lotus was an important food source for Indians, who dug up the starchy roots with their feet. Young shoots were eaten as "greens"; unripe seeds taste like chestnuts and when ripe can be hulled and roasted. Wildfowl eat the seeds, and large colonies are important nurseries for fish and other aquatic life as well as shelter for ducks.

Nelumbo, word of Ceylonese origin for the Hindu lotus; *lutea,* Latin, "yellow."

Nuphar luteum (67) Spatterdock
May–Oct.

Habitat: margins of ponds, lakes, sloughs, streams; along and south of Missouri River.

Flowers: at or just above water surface, deep yellow, saucer- or globe-shaped, to 3" (8 cm) across; sepals 5 or 6, overlapping and much larger than the many petals. Many stamens around a large, compound ovary.

Leaves: egg- to heart-shaped with a wide, basal V-notch, of variable size.

Roots: starchy; were eaten by Indians, as were the seeds. The latter are consumed by deer, muskrat, beaver, raccoons and wildfowl.

Nuphar, name of Arabic origin, originally applied to a European species; *luteum,* Latin, "yellow."

Evening Primrose Family *Onagraceae*

Mostly herbs worldwide, even in very cold climates; concentrated in North America with 18 genera and about 640 species. For floral detail see page 10. Fuchsias and several evening primroses are cultivated. Missouri has six genera and 27 species.

Gaura biennis (49) Gaura, Butterfly Flower
June–Oct.

Habitat: open woods, fields, glades, roadsides in dry or moist areas; throughout Missouri except Bootheel. Erect stalk, branched near top, to 5 feet (1.5 m) tall.

Flowers: on long, many-flowered spikes, 4-merous. The 4 petals white at first, turning pink; recurved, about 5/8" (18 mm) long, while 8 stamens point forward, curving downward, simulating a small butterfly.

Leaves: sessile with small leaflets arising from base of large leaves; lanceolate with widely spaced teeth, to 4" (10 cm) long.

Gaura, Greek, "stately"; *biennis,* Latin, "2-yearly," the life cycle of the species.

Ludwigia alternifolia (72) False Loosestrife, Seedbox
June–Aug.

Habitat: wet places, fields, swamps, sloughs, ditches; statewide. Erect, branched, to about 2½ feet (75 cm) tall. Does well as a garden subject, seeding freely.

Flowers: 4-merous, usually single, on very short peduncles from leaf axils. Base of flower swollen (a hypanthium); 4 bright yellow petals.

Leaves: lanceolate, to 4" (10 cm) long, alternate, pointed, tapering at base to hardly noticeable stems.

Fruit: a 4-sided capsule which remains on the plant through the winter ("seedbox").

Onagraceae

Ludwigia, for the German botanist C.G. Ludwig who lived in the 18th century; *alternifolia,* Latin, "alternate leaved."

Oenothera: Of 12 species in Missouri, 4 have very limited distribution. Flowers open in the evening and close during the next morning. All have prominently 4-lobed stigmas. A few open nights only.

Oenothera biennis (72) Evening Primrose
June–Oct.

Habitat: fields, prairies, waste places, rights of way; statewide. Stalk robust, much-branched, leafy, to 6 feet (1.8 m) tall.

Flowers: several to many in terminal racemes, light yellow, 4-petaled, subtended by narrow, recurved bracts. The petals are rounded.

Leaves: alternate, sessile or with very short petioles, lanceolate, light green, with insignificant teeth or without, to 6" (15 cm) long.

Horticulture selections with much larger flowers are being developed.

Oenothera, Greek, "wine-scented," a characteristic of some species; *biennis,* Latin, "2-yearly," the life cycle of the species.

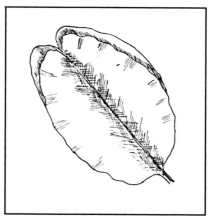

Oenothera macrocarpa, fruit; actual size 3".

Oenothera macrocarpa (62) Missouri Evening Primrose
May–Aug.
(Formerly *O. missouriensis*)

Habitat: limestone glades of Ozarks and east-central Missouri, north to Missouri River. A dominant, sprawling plant of glades.

Flowers: arise singly from leaf axils, have large, yellow petals and are up to 3½" (9 cm) across. What appears as a long peduncle is actually a tubular part of the flower with the ovary hidden at the leaf axil. Turns orange on fading.

Fruit: showy, 4-winged capsule, about 2" (5½ cm) long.
Leaves: alternate, lanceolate, many on a stem, to 4" (8 cm) long.

macrocarpa, Greek, "large fruited."

Oenothera speciosa (95) Showy Evening Primrose
May–July

Habitat: fields, waste areas, rights of way; southern and eastern counties, rare in northern. Low-growing, either trailing or upright, to 1½ feet (45 cm) tall.
Flowers: usually single, from upper leaf axils on long peduncle, 4-petaled, large, pink or white, to 3" (7½ cm) across.
Leaves: linear to lanceolate, tapering to a petiolelike base, coarsely toothed.

The species is frequently seen along rights of way, covering large areas. Garden selections are being developed.

speciosa, Latin, "showy."

Oenothera laciniata Cutleaved Evening Primrose
May–Oct.

Habitat: fields, waste places, rights of way; absent from northern counties. Usually a low-growing plant, but sometimes to 2 feet (60 cm) tall.
Flowers: few, sessile, in axils of upper leaves, single, 4-petaled, yellow, small.
Leaves: alternate, deeply lobed to near pinnate (featherlike) or coarsely toothed, to 3" (8 cm) long.

laciniata, Latin, "deeply cut" (the leaves).

Oenothera linifolia Thread-leaved Sundrop
May–July

Habitat: fields, prairies, roadsides; generally south of Missouri River. Fragile annual to about 1 foot (30 cm) high, with some branching toward the top.
Flowers: many spaced singly along a long raceme, light yellow, subtended by a very small bract.
Leaves: linear, several arising from one point, threadlike, readily shed under adverse weather conditions.

linifolia, Latin, "linear leaved."

Wood Sorrel Family *Oxalidaceae*

Mostly tropical and subtropical, but also temperate zone herbs of three genera and about 900 species, 800 of them of the wood sorrel genus (*Oxalis*). Leaves often cloverlike, 3-divided. Flowers 5-merous, with 10 stamens united at their base. Stamens and pistils often di- and trimorphic, of different lengths in flowers of the same plant. Some *Oxalis* are house and garden plants. Missouri has four species of the genus *Oxalis*.

Oxalis violacea (91) Violet Wood Sorrel
April–July

Habitat: open woods, fields, rights of way, usually in acid soil; statewide. A low herb with many flowers.
Flowers: in umbel-like groups on long stalks, much higher than the leaves, 5-petaled, light magenta or lavender, rarely white (but never violet), showy.
Leaves: trifoliate (like clover), the leaflets heart-shaped, able to close along the central vein.
Fruit: a fairly long, upright capsule, surrounded by the calyx.

Oxalis, Greek, "sharp" the sour taste caused by oxalic acid in the plants; *violacea*, Latin, "violet."

Oxalis stricta (61) Yellow Wood Sorrel, Sheep Sorrel
May–Oct.

Habitat: open woods, fields, waste places, rights of way; statewide. Herbaceous plant to 8" (20 cm) tall.
Flowers: in unevenly branched umbels on long stems, with 5 yellow, rounded petals.
Leaves: trifoliate, like clover, the leaflets heart-shaped, light to dark green or copper to purple, often recurved, sometimes grayish hairs. The leaflets can and do close along their median axil.
Fruit: an upright, pointed capsule about 1" (3 cm) long.

stricta, Latin, "erect."

Poppy Family *Papaveraceae*

Herbs and a few shrubs in the north-temperate zone, containing a milky juice (latex), of 26 genera and about 250 species. Flowers usually solitary, showy with 4–12 petals, crumpled in the bud, and two sepals which fall off as the flowers open. Many stamens; ovary superior. *Papaver somniferum* (Latin, "sleep-bringing poppy") is the source of opium. Other species provide oils. Many poppies are cultivated. Missouri has only the two genera and two species treated below.

Sanguinaria canadensis (28) Bloodroot
March–April

Habitat: on rich, wooded slopes and valleys; statewide except northeast and Southeast Lowlands.

Flowers: open before or just as the leaves start to unfurl. As it opens, 2 sepals fall off and from 8–16 petals of uneven size and length descend to a horizontal position, forming a flower that grows to 1¼" (3½ cm) across. Many yellow stamens. Because petals are of uneven length one often finds square-shaped flowers. Each flower lasts only 1 day.

Leaves: originally wrapped around the stem unfurl into a many-lobed, dark green horizontal position to 8" (20 cm) wide; persist to mid-summer.

Roots: horizontal, fleshy tubers; fingerlike, with a senna-red juice, used by Indians as a dye, thus "bloodroot."

sanguinaria, Latin, *sanguis,* "blood."

Stylophorum diphyllum (58) Celandine Poppy
April–June

Habitat: wooded slopes, moist wooded valleys of central and southeast counties. Much-branched, soft-stemmed herb to 18" (45 cm) tall.

Flowers: single or a few arise from leaf axils, with 4 bright yellow, rounded petals and many stamens, about 2" (5 cm) across, very showy.

Leaves: the basal on long stems, pinnately divided almost to midrib with many lobed or toothed segments. Stem leaves similar to basal but smaller and only 2 on a stem. Leaf color is blue-green, underside silvery gray.

Roots: fleshy, shapeless rhizomes, very large. All parts of the species contain an orange juice. An excellent garden subject if provided with humus-rich soil. Under cultivation the plant will thrive in partial sun and flower through mid-summer.

Stylophorum, Greek, "style-bearing"; *diphyllum,* Greek, "2-leaved" (the stem leaves).

Pokeweed Family *Phytolaccaceae*

Small family with 22 genera and about 125 species in the tropics and subtropics, with only one member in North America. Floral details of the four subfamilies vary so much that description of our species must suffice. Some species have medicinal use, others provide dyes.

Phytolacca americana (80) Pokeweed
May–Oct.

Habitat: waste places, farmyards, fields, rights of way; statewide. Smooth, tall, to 10 feet (3 m), red-stemmed, branched.
Flowers: in terminal and lateral racemes, minute, with greenish-white petals, suffused pink, and 10 protruding stamens and 10 pistils; somewhat bell-shaped.
Leaves: many, smooth, oblong-lanceolate, to 1 foot (3 dm) long, on petioles.
Fruit: dark purple berries, eaten by birds and animals, also used for food coloring and a dye.
Root: has been used in the past as medicine.

Young shoots are eaten by many people, but all mature parts are believed to be poisonous.

Phytolacca, Greek, *phyton*, "plant"; *lacca* refers to the red juice of the berries, which resembles that obtained from the insect *Tachardia lacca*, formerly used as an important dye.

Plantain Family *Plantaginaceae*

Herbs of the temperate zones and mountains in the tropics, of three genera with about 253 species of which 250 belong to the genus *Plantago*. Leaves mostly parallel-veined, basal, narrow or wide. Flowers scapose (on bare stalks), in spikes, minute. For details see description below. The family has no economic significance, mostly considered as weeds. Missouri has one genus, *Plantago*, with ten species.

Plantago Key
1a) Leaves lanceolate on long petioles . . . . *lanceolata*
1b) Leaves broad-ovate
    2a) flower spikes very long to 1 foot (30 cm) . . . . *rugelii*
    2b) flower spikes much shorter to 3" (8 cm) . . . . *virginica*
1c) Leaves linear or very narrow
    3a) spikes densely set with flowers and very long bracts . *aristata*
    3b) spikes loosely set with flowers and very short bracts . . *pusilla*

Plantago lanceolata (35) English Plantain
April–Oct.

Habitat: fields, waste places, rights of way; statewide.
Flowers: in spikes, terminal on scapes (stems without leaves) of tiny, white flowers with a 4-parted corolla. The brown appearance due to many short bracts subtending each flower.
Leaves: basal in a rosette, lanceolate with parallel veins and long, tapering petioles. One of the few dicotyledons with parallel veining.

Plantago, Latin, "footlike," the broad leaves of some species; *lanceolata*, Latin, "lance-shaped."

Plantago rugelii Rugel Plantain
May–Oct.

Habitat: almost any sunny place; statewide.
Flowers: on scapes to 18" (45 cm) long in spikes; similar to *P. lanceolata*
Leaves: broadly egg-shaped with parallel veining on long stalks.

rugelii for the botanist Ferdinand Rugel, German (1806–1879).

Plantago virginica Hoary Plantain
April–June

Habitat: any sunny locality; statewide.
Flowers: very similar to *P. rugelii* with a much shorter inflorescence, on scapes to 6" (15 cm).
Leaves: obovate to oblanceolate (NOT round), narrowing toward base into a short petiole, a few with inconspicuous teeth.

Plantago aristata Bracted Plantain
May–Nov.

Habitat: any sunny locality; statewide.
Flowers: similar to *P. lanceolata,* but with long, much protruding bracts tipped with bristles, on scapes to 9" (25 cm) long.
Leaves: basal, very narrow, without stems.

aristata, Greek, "tipped with spines," (the fruit).

Plantago pusilla Slender Plantain
April–June

Habitat: acid soil, rock outcroppings, glades, sandstone ledges; south of Missouri River and north-central counties. A miniature plantain, to 6" (15 cm) high.
Flowers: spaced along the scape (not crowded).
Leaves: linear.

pusilla, Latin, "very small."

Phlox Family *Polemoniaceae*

Mostly herbs and a few shrubs of North America, Eurasia, and a few in South America, of 18 genera with about 300 species. Flowers often showy, 5-merous of united petals with five lobes. Stamens inserted in corolla tube; ovary superior. Many species and their cultivars used in gardens. Missouri has three genera and ten species.

Polemoniaceae

Phlox bifida (107) Sand Phlox
March–May

Habitat: dry upland woods, wooded or open slopes, mainly on acid but also on lime soils; in southeastern Ozarks and north-central counties. To about 6" (15 cm) high, spreading, forming mats.
Flowers: pale purple, 5-lobed, each lobe with a rounded, V-shaped notch.
Leaves: many, opposite, linear; very short, light green.

Phlox, Greek, "flame"; *bifida,* Latin, "twice-cut," the flower lobes.

Phlox divaricata (107) Blue Phlox, Wild Sweet William
April–June

Habitat: open woods, wet streamsides, bottomlands; statewide except Southeast Lowlands. Grows to 1 foot (3 dm) tall, usually in partial or full shade, but sometimes in full sun.
Flowers: 5-lobed, the lobes somewhat heart-shaped, with or without fine notches, in varying colors: pale blue-purple, red-purple, rose-lavender, rarely white.
Leaves: opposite, lanceolate, spaced apart, to 2" (5 cm) long. Dark green, leafy shoots spread from base and take root.

divaricata, Latin, "spreading."

Phlox pilosa Downy Phlox
July–Oct.

Habitat: appearance, floral details are identical to *P. divaricata* but leaves and stems are covered by spreading hair, while *P. divaricata* is smooth. *P. pilosa* comes into bloom somewhat later than the *P. divaricata.* Besides the colors rose, red-purple and light-violet, there is a white form with a purple center.

pilosa, Latin, "soft hairy."

Phlox paniculata (103) Perennial Phlox
July–Oct.

Habitat: borders of woods, streamsides, below bluffs, gravel bars; generally south of Missouri River and east-central counties. A tall, late-blooming phlox from 2–4 feet (6 dm–1.2 m) tall. *P. paniculata* has many horticultural cultivars in a great variety of colors.
Flowers: in dense, pyramidal, terminal clusters (thus *"paniculata"*), in many shades of purple, red-purple, rose and rarely white.
Leaves: opposite, sessile, oblong to lanceolate, prominently veined, spaced apart on stems.

paniculata, Latin, "in panicles."

Polemonium reptans (108) Jacob's Ladder
April–June

Habitat: usually in moist, wooded bottomlands or bases of slopes, wooded valleys; statewide. Low, weak-stemmed plants to 15" (near 4 dm) high.
Flowers: in loose terminal clusters, bell-shaped, 5-lobed short tubes, light blue to blue-lavender.
Leaves: basal and stem leaves pinnately compound with opposite, ovate, smooth leaflets. The basal leaves on long petioles.

Polemonium, Greek, of unknown meaning; *reptans,* Latin, "creeping," though the plant does NOT creep. Jacob's ladder has 2 explanations: the ladder on which the biblical Jacob saw angels ascending to heaven, or the name of a nautical instrument for sighting celestial positions; both refer to the ladderlike position of the leaflets.

Milkwort Family *Polygalaceae*

Herbs, shrubs, small trees, climbers and saprophytes of worldwide distribution except the arctic. About 17 genera and 1,000 species. Flowers irregular, of five unequal sepals and two usually look-alike petals. Our species have three petals joined to the stamens, which are enclosed in a sheath. Ovary superior. Missouri has one genus with five species.

Polygala sanguinea (94) Milkwort
May–Oct.

Habitat: dry or wet situations, old fields, meadows, glades, prairies, often on acid soils; statewide except northwest counties. Each plant has usually only 1 stem, to about 8" (20 cm) high.
Flowers: in terminal, dense racemes, pink, white or greenish. For floral details see family description above.
Leaves: alternate, widely spaced, linear to narrowly elliptical.

Another species, *P. senega,* was used by Indians as a remedy for snakebite. It is still being collected by root diggers. The common name is snakeroot.

Polygala, Greek, "much milk," refers to a plant which was supposed to increase milk production; *sanguinea,* Latin, "blood-red" (which the species is NOT).

Buckwheat Family *Polygonaceae*

Some 30 genera with about 750 species, mainly North American and Eurasian. Ours are herbs with a sour juice and entire leaves without stipules. For floral details see page 12. Few species are in horticultural use. Rhubarb and buckwheat are edible. Missouri has six genera with 35 species.

Polygonum: There are 24 species in Missouri, 10 of them widely distributed and described below. Many species provide important food sources for wildfowl. *Polygonum,* Greek, "many knees" (the swollen nodes).

Polygonum Key

1a) Stems erect
    2a) stems with prickles . . . . *sagittatum*
    2b) stems without prickles
        3a) leaves wide or heart-shaped
            1) flowers rose or rose-red . . . . *coccineum*
            2) flowers greenish . . . . *virginianum*
        3b) leaves linear or lanceolate, joints with bristles
            1) stems erect, racemes interrupted near base . . . *punctatum*
            2) stems ascending from trailing base, racemes inter-
            rupted . . . . *hydropiperoides*
            3) leaves with dark patches . . . . *persicaria*
        3c) leaves linear or lanceolate, joints without bristles
            1) spikes arching or pendulous . . . . *lapathifolium*
            2) spikes erect . . . . *pensylvanicum*
            3) flowers in leaf-axils . . . . *tenue*
1b) stems trailing or climbing . . . . *scandens*

Polygonum pensylvanicum Pinkweed
May–Oct.

Habitat: moist to wet, open bottomlands; statewide. Tall, erect, branched, to 6 feet (1.8 m) tall.
Flowers: in many erect racemes, to about 1½" (3 cm) long, pink or white.
Leaves: lanceolate on short stems. Peduncles either hairy or with glands. Joints often red, without prickles.

Polygonum punctatum Water Smartweed
July–Nov.

Habitat: wet, open bottomlands, borders of lakes, sloughs; statewide. Often standing in water, erect stems, single or branched, to 3 feet (9 dm) tall.
Flowers: greenish-white. The sepals with many dots. Racemes very slender, much interrupted, with few flowers, sometimes slightly drooping.
Leaves: narrow lanceolate, to 8" (20 cm) long. Sheaths at the joints with prominent bristles.

    punctatum, Latin, "dotted" (the sepals).

Polygonum persicaria Lady's Thumb
May–Oct.

Habitat: wet, open bottomlands; scattered through central and southern Missouri, and northwestern counties. Native of Europe. Stems erect, usually much-branched, to 2½ feet (75 cm) high, reddish, smooth.
Flowers: in many short, dense spikes, pink to dull rose. Mature sepals show a prominent basal network.
Leaves: usually with dark blotches, narrow lanceolate. Papery sheaths at joints fringed with bristles.

persicaria, Latin, "peachlike," the leaves.

Polygonum hydropiperoides Wild Water Pepper
June–Nov.

Habitat: wet, open bottomlands, stream- and lakesides; scattered throughout Missouri. The name is easily confused with *P. hydropiper.* Stems to 3 feet (9 dm) tall, ascending from the lower part on the ground with roots at the nodes.
Flowers: on slender, often interrupted racemes, minute, off-white to pink.
Leaves: lanceolate to linear on petioles.

Avoid getting any part of the plant in the mouth. Severe swelling will result.

hydropiperoides, hydro-, Greek, "water," *-piperoides,* Latin with a Greek ending, "like pepper."

Polygonum scandens (50) Climbing False Buckwheat
July–Nov.

Habitat: moist, open or shaded bottomlands, alluvial valleys, floodplains; statewide. A rampant climber often forming curtainlike masses of twining, red stems, covering shrubs and trees.
Flowers: minute but produced in large masses on long racemes so that the effect is showy. Flowers are green-white with a 5-parted calyx whose outer 3 segments are strongly winged, contributing much to the overall floral cluster.
Leaves: ovate to heart-shaped, to 6" (15 cm) long.
Fruit: a jet black, shiny seed, which looks and tastes like buckwheat.

scandens, Latin, "climbing."

Polygonum sagittatum Arrow-leaved Tear-thumb
June–Aug.

Habitat: any moist or wet and sunny area; absent from northwestern and most southwestern counties. Weak stems with vicious prickles, often over 3 feet (9 dm) tall.
Flowers: in small clusters at terminal of long stems, pink to whitish green.

Polygonaceae

Leaves: narrow, arrow-shaped with prominent lobes at base, spread far apart. Midrib on underside with weak prickles.

sagittatum, Latin, "arrow-shaped."

Polygonym coccineum (101) Water Smartweed
June–Oct.

Habitat: any wet, open land, streamsides, shores of lakes, ponds and sloughs; statewide except some Ozark counties. Known as a terrestrial and an aquatic plant. Forms dense colonies covering large areas; stems about 40" (1 m), branched.
Flowers: in long, erect racemes, rich pink, rarely white, showy.
Leaves: ovate, sharply pointed, on stems.

coccineum, Latin, "red."

Polygonum virginianum Virginia Knotweed
July–Oct.

Habitat: open woods, rights of way, borders of woods, urban areas; statewide. This species is NOT found in bottomlands as are most others. Stems erect to 40" (1 m) tall, usually leaning.
Flowers: spaced on a very long, nearly linear inflorescence, greenish white, the inflorescence often 10" (25 cm) long.
Leaves: large ovate on short stems. Sheaths at joints are fringed.

Polygonum tenue Slender Knotweed
June–Oct.

Habitat: on dry acid soils of the Ozarks. Stems 4-angled, with ascending or erect branches, very slender, to 1 foot (30 cm) high.
Flowers: insignificant, in leaf axils, greenish.
Leaves: almost linear, folded along midrib, only 1" (2 cm) long.

tenue, Latin, "slim" or "thin."

Polygonum lapathifolium Pale Smartweed
June–Nov.

Habitat: moist bottomlands; statewide but only scattered in Ozarks. Stems branching, sprawling, to 6 feet (1.8 m) long. Sheaths at joints neither hairy nor with bristles.
Flowers: in pendulous and arching dense inflorescences, greenish white or pink. The outer 2 sepals strongly 3-veined, each of which is divided at the top into 2 recurving branches.
Leaves: variable linear, lauceolate or elliptical on petioles.

lapathifolium, Latin, "with leaves of a *Lapathium,*" a member of the sorrel (*Rumex*) genus.

Rumex: Missouri has 13 species, of which the 3 below have a wide distribution. Flowers are so small and differences so immaterial that identification is best accomplished by leaf shapes.

Rumex acetosella Sheep Sorrel
May–Sept.

Habitat: in waste places and fallow fields; statewide. Native of Europe. Much lower than the above, to about 1½ feet (4½ dm) high.
Flowers: spaced apart on a long inflorescence.
Leaves: small, arrow-shaped (see drawing).

acetosella, Latin, "slightly acid."

Rumex altissimus (79) Pale Dock
April–May

Habitat: fields, waste places, alluvial soils; mostly north of Missouri River, scattered elsewhere. About 3 feet (9 dm) tall, with short branches.
Flowers: in an elongated inflorescence of many whorls, of 6 sepals in 2 rows, no petals and 6 stamens. The wind-carried pollen contributes to hay fever suffering.
Leaves: lanceolate, on petioles, pointed and narrowed toward base.
Fruit: a 3-winged envelope of 1–3 "grains." Indians made a gruel of the seeds. The entire plant turns rich brown after flowering. The wind-carried pollen contributes to hay fever sufferers.

Rumex, the Roman name for dock; *altissimus,* Latin, "tallest."

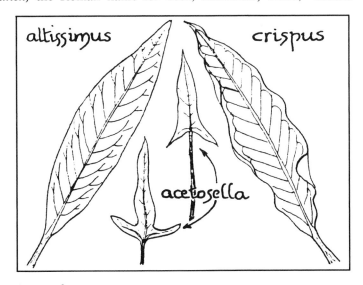

Rumex leaves

Rumex crispus Sour Dock
April–May

Native of Europe. All data as for *R. altissimus,* but leaves are conspicuously wavy and wrinkled, the larger ones wider than those of *R. altissimus* and rounded at base.

crispus, Latin, "curled."

Purslane Family *Portulacaceae*

About 19 genera with 500 species; succulent herbs and some shrubs, mainly in South Africa and the Americas. All species except *Claytonia* have tissue-paperlike stipules, two sepals, four to six petals (five in our species), with as many stamens as petals, or more, and a more or less superior ovary. *Portulaca grandiflora* is a garden variety. Missouri has three genera with seven species.

Claytonia virginica (23) Spring Beauty
Feb.–May

Habitat: open woods, fields, valleys, suburban lawns; statewide. About 5" (13 cm) high during flowering but about twice that high later. The most widely distributed early spring flower.
Flowers: with 2 sepals which fall off as the flower opens, 5 petals, white with distinct pink veining, (sometimes the petals are also pink); 5 pink stamens.
Leaves: 1 or 2 basal and 1 opposite pair on stems, narrow lanceolate, tapering to a sessile base, dark green, fleshy.
Root: a rounded corm, edible, used as food by Indians. The leaves are also edible.

Claytonia for John Clayton (1685–1773), pioneer American botanist.

Talinum calycinum (95) Rock Pink, Fame Flower
May–Aug.

Habitat: sandstone and chert outcroppings with acid soils, south of Missouri River. Succulent plant with naked flower stalks (scape), to 1 foot (3 dm), growing out of rock crevices without apparent soil.
Flowers: in open, terminal groups, with 2 sepals shed at opening, 5 cherry-red petals, and many stamens. Flowers do not open until about noon even on sunny days.
Leaves: basal, fleshy, awl-like to 2" (5 cm) long.
Root: a thick rhizome, like a miniature German iris root.

Talinum, supposed to be derived from the name of an African member of the family (Gleason); *calycinum,* Greek, "like a calyx," the sepals.

Talinum parviflorum Rock Pink, Fame Flower

All data same as for *T. calycinum,* but flowers are smaller and have only 4–8 stamens.

parviflorum, Latin, "small-flowered."

Primrose Family *Primulaceae*

Some 28 genera with about 1,000 species of the north-temperate zone with many alpine species. Flowering stalks usually scapes (without leaves), leaves often in basal rosettes. Flowers 5-merous, petals united with five lobes; stamens set in corolla in line with lobes. Lobes sharply recurved in shooting star (*Dodecatheon*) and *Cyclamen.* Ovary superior or semi-inferior. *Cyclamen* and primroses are much cultivated. Missouri has six genera with 14 species.

Anagallis arvensis (98) Pimpernel, Poor Man's Weatherglass
May–Sept.

Habitat: fields, pastures, waste places, rights of way of central and east-central Missouri. Native of Europe. Tender annual, branched from the base, to about 6" (15 cm) high.

Flowers: terminal and arising single on long stems from leaf axils; deeply 5-lobed, very small, scarlet or brick-red, rarely white. They close around 4 p.m. or whenever clouds shade the sun (thus the originally British common name).

Leaves: opposite, sessile, ovate with dots underneath, only to ¾" (2 cm) long.

Fruit: a tiny capsule that opens its "lid" to disperse seeds.

Anagallis, Greek, "delight-again," referring to the closing and reopening of the flowers; *arvensis,* Latin, "of the field."

Dodecatheon meadia (89) Shooting Star
April–June

Habitat: prairies, glades, bluffs, open wooded slopes in eastern, central and southern Missouri. Plants often seen in woods; will not flower well in shaded areas.

Flowers: in umbels on long scapes to 2 feet (6 dm) high which arise from basal leaves, with 5 petal-like, large lobes recurved upward. Stamens and pistil protrude from tube downward, giving the "shooting star" appearance. Color pink or white. Plants and flowers on prairies are much more robust and larger than those growing on glades.

Leaves: basal, long-ovate to spatulate, narrowed toward base, the midrib often tinted red.

Dodecatheon, Greek, "12 gods" (reason unknown); *meadia,* (which, properly, should be *meadii*) in honor of Dr. Richard Mead (1673–1754).

Lysimachia lanceolata (65) Loosestrife
May–Aug.

Habitat: wet or dry open woods, wet areas of prairies and fields, absent from northwest counties. Upright, unbranched herb to 2 feet (6 dm) tall.
Flowers: arise singly from upper leaf axils with 5 yellow, pointed lobes; showy.
Leaves: opposite, closely spaced; the lower ovate, becoming lanceolate higher up on the stem, much narrowed toward base. Plant sends out runners (stolons),

> *Lysimachia* is believed to be named for Lysimachos, king of Thrace; *lanceolata,* Latin, "lance-shaped." Loosestrife is a mistranslation of the botanical name.

Lysimachia ciliata Fringed Loosestrife
May–July

Habitat: in moist or wet areas either in open woods or open valleys; statewide. Herb about 3 feet (9 dm) tall.
Flowers: very similar to *L. lanceolata* but lobes are minutely fringed. Stems are hairy. The inflorescence is spread out.
Leaves: broad ovate with petioles to 6" (15 cm) long. Petioles are long-hairy.

> *ciliata,* Latin, "with eyebrowlike hair."

Wintergreen Family *Pyrolaceae*

A very small family of four genera with 30 species, mostly of the north-temperate zone and in the arctic. Flowers of four or five sepals and petals and eight to ten stamens inserted opposite the sepals and petals. Ovary superior. Missouri has one genus with two species.

Monotropa uniflora (51) Indian Pipe
Aug.-Oct.

Habitat: dry, humus-rich woods, mainly oak-hickory; absent from west-central Missouri. A plant unable to produce chlorophyll, living off decaying matter; a saprophyte.
Flowers: single on a white scaly stem to 8" (20 cm) tall, urn-shaped, nodding, 4 or 5 petals, no sepals. Flowers are white, turning purple and later black. As seeds ripen the wilted flower often turns upright.
Leaves: none, replaced by scales on the floral stem.

> *Monotropa,* Greek, "single turn," the nodding flower; *uniflora,* Latin, "one-flowered."

Crowfoot Family *Ranunculaceae*

Some 60 genera of herbs and a few climbers with about 1,800 species worldwide, mainly in temperate zone of northern hemisphere. Family characteristics are confusing and inconsistent. Floral shapes are incredibly variable; petals are either present or absent, ovaries often reduced to one- or two-seeded carpelets. For more floral details, see page 16. Many horticultural subjects: anemone, clematis, columbine, Christmas rose, aconite, winter aconite, larkspur, trollius, pasque flower and others. Missouri has 15 genera with 43 species.

Actaea pachypoda (47) White Baneberry, Doll's Eyes
May–June

Habitat: rich woods, ravines, usually on north-facing slopes; eastern one-half of Missouri. Single-stemmed, to 30" (7½ dm) tall.

Flowers: in a tight, rounded inflorescence on a long stem with many flowers. Sepals and petals fall off as the flowers open, leaving a mass of stamens and the pistils; white.

Leaves: 3-times compound (3-ternate) on very long stems with both lateral and terminal leaflets which are oblong; coarsely toothed on petioles.

Fruit: white berries with a black "eye," each on a dark red stalk (the "doll's eyes").

The berries may be poisonous, thus "baneberry."

Actaea, Greek, originally the name of the elder plant; *pachypoda,* Greek, "short-footed," the berries.

Anemone canadensis (36) White Anemone
May–July

Habitat: river floodplains or other moist situations, mainly along the Mississippi and Missouri rivers and their tributaries. The species covers large areas on dikes of the Mississippi River in northeastern Missouri. Leafy perennial to 3 feet (75 cm) tall but usually lower.

Flowers: single, on long stems from upper leaf axils, typical anemone type, with 5 sepals acting as petals; white, with many stamens.

Leaves: the basal on long stems, 3-divided, with further incisions and coarse teeth. Stem leaves similar but sessile.

Anemone, Greek, "wind," short for wind-flower.

Anemone caroliniana Prairie Anemone
March–May

Habitat: prairies and fields with acid soil; southwest Missouri. Herb to about 1 foot (30 cm) tall.

Ranunculaceae

Flowers: one on a stem, white, tinged lavender, pink or rose, with many sepals (10–20).
Leaves: the basal on long stems, deeply divided into many sections; stem-leaves sessile about half way up the stem.

Anemone virginiana (31) Thimbleweed
April–Aug.

Habitat: open woods on slopes or in valleys; statewide. Herbs on erect, unbranched stalks, to 3 feet (9 dm) tall.
Flowers: about 1" (25 mm) across, usually from 1 to 3 with 5 off-white sepals and a domed center of many carpelets, thus "thimbleweed."
Leaves: 3-divided with deeply cleft and large-toothed leaflets, both basal and caudal (stem) leaves on petioles, the basal on very long stems.
Fruit: the fluffy, white mass of seeds often remains on the stalk through the winter.

Anemonella thalictroides (24) Rue Anemone
March–June

Habitat: open wooded slopes; statewide except northwest and Southeast Lowlands. An early flowering, delicate plant to 9" (28 cm) tall but usually much lower. It is normally absent from bottomlands. Often confused with *Isopyrum* (see box below).
Flowers: quite variable, with from 5 to 10 sepals, white or magenta-pink. The sepals may be pointed or sometimes rounded. Stamens many, yellowish green. Flowers in small umbels which are subtended by a whorl of nearly round, sessile leaf bracts.
Leaves: basal on erect stems, 3-lobed, much like the bracts. The basal leaves appear after flowering has begun.

Anemonella is possibly the longest flowering species of early spring.

Anemonella, Greek, "little windflower"; *thalictroides,* Greek, "like a *Thalictrum*" (the leaves).

Isopyrum biternatum (24) False Rue Anemone
March–May

Habitat: mainly at base of wooded slopes or in wooded bottomlands, sometimes in sunny situations; statewide except Southeast Lowlands. Often confused with *Anemonella* (see box below). Plants 5-8" (13–20 cm) high, often in large colonies.
Flowers: 5 white sepals arising on long stems from leaf axils.
Leaves: basal and cauline (stem); while *Anemonella* has only bracts on flowering stems, *Isopyrum* has stem-leaves. Both types are 2-or 3-divided, compound with rounded lobes. Stem leaves often sessile.

Isopyrum, Greek, name of a *Fumaria*, which has similar leaves; *biternatum,* Latin, "twice in sets of three," the leaves and their divisions.

How to distinguish RUE ANEMONE from FALSE RUE ANEMONE		
	Rue Anemone *Anemonella*	**False Rue Anemone** *Isopyrum*
Habitat	wooded slopes	moist bottomlands
Occurrence	single plants	in colonies
Leaves on Stems with Flowers	none, only bracts below flowers	present, compound
Sepals	5-10	5
Color	white or pink	always white

Aquilegia canadensis (91) Columbine
April–July

Habitat: limestone ledges, rocky slopes in woods, ravines, bluffs; state-wide except Southeast Lowlands. The species exists from the Atlantic to the Pacific. Plants up to 2 feet (6 dm) tall, often hanging from cliffs.

Flowers: single on long stems, of 5 petals forming elongate, hollow spurs containing nectar; 5 sepals are leaflike, appended to the petals, and light yellow while the other floral parts are red.

Leaves: a few basal, the others caudal (stem), both on long petioles, 3-divided with deep lobes, blue-green.

Aquilegia, Latin, either from *aquila,* "eagle" for the floral spurs, or from *aqua,* "water" and *legere,* "to collect," for the fluid in the hollow spurs.

Clematis fremontii (30) Fremont's Leather Flower
April–May

Habitat: on limestone glades of the eastern part of Missouri. *C. fremontii* is found in large quantities only in a few counties south and west of St. Louis. A very similar species grows in Kansas and Nebraska. The only non-climbing *Clematis* in the state, bushlike on open glades with stalks up to 2 feet (6 dm) tall.

Flowers: sometimes ascending, usually hanging on short stems, of 5 sepals densely hairy on their margins, lavender or white, bell-shaped.

Leaves: broad ovate on very short stems, long-lasting, to nearly 5" (13 cm) long, opposite. Dried leaves stay on plant with only the filigree of their veining remaining.

Clematis, Greek, name of a climbing plant; *fremontii* for the American explorer and General John Charles Fremont, 1813–1890.

Ranunculaceae

Delphinium tricorne (108) Larkspur
April–June

Habitat: open wooded slopes, ledges, streamsides, below bluffs; statewide. Starts flowering at 6-10" (15-25 cm) but may reach to 18" (45 cm) later.

Flowers: irregular, 5 sepals form the showy flowers while the petals are reduced to inconsequential appendages. One sepal provides a long spur. Few to many flowers, terminal along a raceme, in shades of blue, violet, white and mixtures of these.

Leaves: few, deeply divided into linear segments.

Bumblebees frequent *Delphinium,* drilling a hole into the spur to collect nectar; bees pollinate the flowers.

Delphinium, Greek, "dolphin," an assumed likeness to the flowers; *tricorne,* Latin, "with 3 horns," also describing the shape of the flower.

Delphinium carolinianum (112) Carolina Larkspur
May–June

Habitat: glades, prairies, fields, rocky slopes, rights of way; along and south of Missouri River. A showy, erect plant to 3 feet (9 dm) tall.

Flowers: with upturned spurs as described for *D. tricorne* in deep blue, violet-lavender, pink, purple or white.

Leaves: well spaced on stems, 3-5, divided into very narrow, linear straps.

Delphinium virescens Prairie Larkspur
May–July

Habitat: prairies, fields, openings in woods in unglaciated western Missouri. Nearly identical to *D. carolinianum,* but flowers are white or greenish white, or tinged with blue or lilac.

virescens, Latin, "greenish."

Hepatica nobilis (24) Liverleaf
March–April

Habitat: steep, wooded slopes, usually facing north or east; absent from western third of state. Flowering stems, extremely hairy, to 6" (15 cm) high. One of the earliest flowering plants in spring.

Flowers: on leafless stems (scapes), which are silky hairy with 5-12 petal-like sepals, numerous stamens, one flower to a scape; white, pink, and shades of lavender.

Leaves: basal on long, hairy stems, deeply 3-lobed with a heart-shaped base, the lobes pointed. Light green at first, on dying they turn leathery in beautiful shades of wine-red and brown and remain so through the winter, surrounding the newly appearing plants in spring.

Hepatica, Latin, "like a liver," the color of the old leaves; *nobilis,* Latin, "noble."

Hydrastis canadensis (36) Golden Seal
April–May

Habitat: humus-rich wooded slopes and wooded valleys; absent from northern and southwestern counties. A herbaceous plant to 1½ feet (45 cm) high.

Flowers: terminal on a short peduncle arising from the axil of 2-leaved plants. The peduncle supports a very small leaf. The flower has no petals; 3 sepals fall off as the flower opens, leaving only white stamens and pistils in a global inflorescence.

Leaves: either 1 or at most 2, near the top of the stem, large, 5-lobed with palmate veins, the lobes with large, coarse teeth. After flowering a few basal leaves of the same shape appear.

The roots are collected by the scourge of our flora, root diggers, for assumed medicinal use. *Hydrastis* sometimes forms very large colonies.

Hydrastis, Greek, refers to hydro, "water," as the plant demands moist situations.

Ranunculus: There are 20 species in Missouri; 8 of them with a fairly wide range.

Ranunculus Key

1a) One or more basal leaves NOT dissected (but having wavy or scalloped margins)
    2a) petals longer than sepals . . . . *harveyi*
    2b) petals shorter than sepals . . . .
        3a) plant glabrous (no hair) . . . . *abortivus*
        3b) plant hairy . . . . *micranthus*
1b) All leaves (including basal) lobed, divided or dissected
    2a) petals showy, longer than sepals
        3a) leaves as wide, or wider than long
            1) plant hairy . . . . *hispidus*
            2) plant glabrous or nearly so . . . . *septentrionalis*
        3b) leaves longer than wide (mostly basal) . . . . . . *fascicularis*
    2b) petals small, shorter or equal to sepals
        3a) plant sparsely hairy . . . . *recurvatus*
        3b) plant glabrous (hairless) . . . . *sceleratus*

Ranunculus harveyi (54) Harvey's Buttercup
March–May

Habitat: in acid soils on wooded slopes, rocky, open areas; south and east-central Missouri. A slender, branched herb about 1 foot (3 dm) high, sometimes taller.

Flowers: 4-8 petals, variable in size, sepals very short, recurved, many stamens and small carpels (containers of usually 1 seed each).

Ranunculaceae

Leaves: the basal on long stems lobed, kidney-shaped; stem leaves either 3-lobed or in straplike segments.

harveyi for Francis Leroy Harvey (1850–1900) who was the first to describe the species.

Ranunculus abortivus Small-flowered Crowfoot
March–June

Habitat: moist ground, streamsides, ditches, waste places, rights of way; statewide. A persistent weed with upright growth, to 20" (4 dm) tall; branched, the entire plant without hair (glabrous),
Flowers: very small with 5 minute petals, yellow with massed small carpels in a domed appearance.
Leaves: basal, round and lobed on thick petioles; stem leaves sessile, usually divided into 3 narrow, irregular lobes.

abortivus, Latin, "imperfect" or "missing," referring to the minute sepals.

Ranunculus micranthus Rock Crowfoot
March–Nov.

Habitat: moist or dry uplands or valleys of central and southern counties. Similar to *R. abortivus,* but the plant is hairy, especially at bases of stems and petioles.

micranthus, Greek, "small-flowered."

Ranunculus hispidus (54) Hispid Buttercup
March–June

Habitat: generally dry woods, ridges, slopes, valleys, on acid and cherty soils; southeast and south-central Missouri. Upright stems, to 1 foot (3 dm) high, densely hairy.
Flowers: 5-petaled, yellow with many stamens; petals often recurved, twice as long as sepals.
Leaves: wide; at times wider than long; 3-divided into ovate, coarsely toothed lobes, the lateral sessile, the terminal may or may not have a very short stem.

hispidus, Latin, "densely hairy."

Ranunculus septentrionalis Swamp or Marsh Buttercup
April–June

Habitat: moist places, valleys, streamsides, ditches; statewide. Similar to *R. hispidus* but with or without a few hairs. Generally a small plant but may reach 1 foot (3 dm).
Flowers: with 5 shiny (wax-covered) petals, yellow.

Leaves: 3-divided, the divisions again with 3 or more sections, coarsely toothed. The lateral leaflets usually petioled, the terminal on a long stem.

septentrionalis, Latin, "northern."

Ranunculus fascicularis Early Buttercup
March–May

Habitat: near streams and in moist bottomlands; statewide. While flowering, 4-8" (10-20 cm) high, later taller.
Flowers: similar to *R. hispidus.*
Leaves: longer than broad, mostly basal, 3- to 5-divided, with linear to oblong rounded segments. Stems and leaves gray-green due to dense hairiness.

fascicularis, Latin, "clustered" or "in bundles."

Ranunculus recurvatus Hooked Crowfoot
May–July

Habitat: alluvial mudflats, gravel bars; south of Missouri River and a few counties north, Ozarks.
Flowers: small, pale yellow.
Leaves and Stems: sparsely hairy, the basal deeply 3-cleft, with broad divisions which are again much-divided with coarse teeth. None of the leaflets have any stalks.

recurvatus, Latin, "recurved," the appearance of the petals.

Ranunculus sceleratus Cursed Crowfoot
May–Aug.

Habitat: moist places primarily along Missouri and Mississippi rivers. Erect, stout, with hollow stems; varying height to 2 feet (6 dm).
Flowers: very small with minute light yellow petals of 1/8" (3 mm) length.
Leaves: both basal and stem deeply 3-parted with lobed, toothed segments. The plant is glabrous (without hair).

sceleratus, Latin, "polluted," the plant poisons cattle and causes skin irritation in humans.

Thalictrum revolutum (83) Waxy Meadow Rue
May–July

Habitat: fields, open woods, rights of way; in northeast counties and south of Missouri River. Several meadow rue species grow in Missouri and look very much alike. Much-branched stems, 5 feet (1.5 m) tall and often taller.

Flowers: uni-sexed, petals and sepals fall off; consist of either stamens or pistils only, in loose clusters, greenish-white or light purple.

Leaves: compound, arising without a common leaf stalk from the main stem. Leaflets divided into 3–5 sections, somewhat egg-shaped with blunt lobes, (reminiscent of rue anemone, *Anemonella thalictroides*). Edges of leaflets are rolled under.

Thalictrum, Greek, used by Pliny and Dioscorides in the first century for a meadow rue; *revolutum*, Latin, "rolled under," the leaflets.

Thalictrum dioicum Early Meadow Rue
April–May

Habitat: rich, north-facing slopes south of Missouri River. Very similar to *T. revolutum*, but the compound leaves of the middle and upper part of the stem are attached to the main stem with long leaf-stalks (petioles).

dioicum, Greek, "having male and female flowers on separate plants."

Buckthorn Family *Rhamnaceae*

About 58 genera with 900 species, mostly shrubs and trees, worldwide, but centered in warm climates. Some have spines (*Rhamnus*). Flowers 4- or 5-merous, ovary superior. Several species provide dyes. *Ceanothus* is often cultivated. Missouri has three genera and six species.

Ceanothus americanus (39) New Jersey Tea
May–Nov.

Habitat: open woods, upland prairies, glades; statewide. Low, much-branched shrub to 3 feet (9 dm) high.

Flowers: on peduncles from leaf axils, those from lower part of stems much longer than upper; in small, rounded panicles of tiny, white flowers, reminiscent of a dwarf lilac.

Leaves: alternate, broadly ovate, sessile, finely toothed, on petioles.

During the revolutionary war a tea was brewed from the leaves.

Ceanothus, Greek, meaning is obscure.

Ceanothus ovatus Redroot
April–June

Habitat: prairies, fields, uplands in western Missouri only. Very similar to *C. americanus*, but somewhat lower with dense, flat-topped inflorescences and leaves that are narrow, oblong to elliptical.

Rose Family *Rosaceae*

About 122 genera and 3,370 species of worldwide distribution, centered in the north-temperate regions. Mostly shrubs and trees, but also herbs. For floral detail see page 12. Many species have stipules and thorns. Our native fruits are mostly of this family: apples, pears, almonds, nectarines, plums, peaches, strawberries, blackberries, raspberries; many garden subjects besides roses. Exclusive of garden escapees and adventives, Missouri has 17 genera and 105 species (but of these, 50 are hawthorns and 16 are blackberries or raspberries).

Amelanchier arborea (27) Shadbush, Serviceberry
March–May

Habitat: open woods, ridges, bluffs; statewide. A multi-stalked large shrub or a small to medium-sized tree.

Flowers: showy, white, of 5 long narrow petals in clusters. Flowers appear before leaves.

Leaves: ovate, finely toothed, 2-4" (5-10 cm) long.

Bark: light gray, smooth on young trees, becoming scaly with ridges in age.

Fruit: red turning purple, sweet and edible, esteemed by wildlife.

"Shadbush" because it flowers at time the shad swim up the eastern rivers to spawn.

Amelanchier, a name apparently adopted from the French Provence; *arborea,* Latin, "tree-forming."

Aruncus dioicus (40) Goat's Beard
May–July

Habitat: moist woods of central, southern and eastern Missouri. Showy, to 5 feet (1.5 m) tall.

Flowers: single-sexed, "male" and "female" on separate plants, in open panicles with very small, 5-petaled flowers, white.

Leaves: compound, the leaflets in threes or fives, both lateral and terminal on long stems; oblong, sharply pointed, finely toothed with very short stems.

Aruncus is a fine garden subject if given a humus-rich soil and shade. There are several unrelated plants in Missouri called goat's beard.

Aruncus, the classical Latin name for the genus; *dioicus,* Greek, an abbreviation of *dioecious,* "separate sexes.

Rosaceae

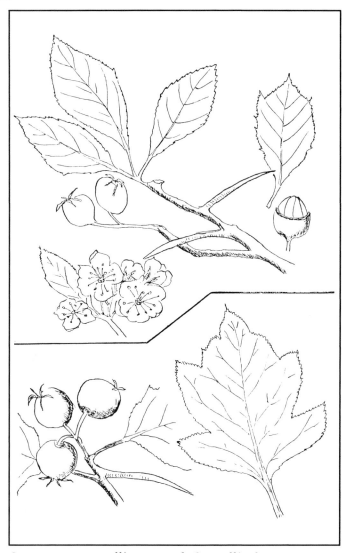

Crataegus crus-galli, top, and *C. mollis,* bottom.

Crataegus species (34) Hawthorn, Red Haw
April–May

Habitat: old fields, roadsides, hedges, thickets; variable. Hawthorn is the state flower of Missouri. There are at present 50 species recognized in the state, a number which may be drastically reduced in the future. Only a few have wide distribution. The 2 species in the drawing are quite common.

Flowers: typical of our fruit trees, with 5 petals, white or pink, many stamens and a thickened base (the hypanthium).

Leaves: alternate, petioled, either egg-shaped or with various lobes, toothed. Many species have thorns but not all.

Fruit: small, applelike, usually not over ½" (12 mm) wide; a favorite food of ducks, pheasants, grouse and many other animals.

Crateagus, Greek, "flowering thorn."

Crataegus crus-galli Cockspur Thorn
May–June

Habitat: thickets, borders of woods, roadsides; statewide except Southeast Lowlands (see drawing). Trees to 8½ yards (8 m) high.

Flowers: (see *Crataegus* species, above), white.

Leaves: shiny on surface, ovate, tapering to base, finely toothed. There are 8 recognized varieties of this species.

crus-galli, Latin, "cock's spur" (the long thorns).

Crataegus mollis Summer Haw
April (only)

Habitat: moist, open land, bottomlands; missing from part of Ozarks. Tree up to 13 yards (12 m) tall.

Flowers: white.

Leaves: broad at base, with 4–6 pointed lobes, finely toothed. Some of the upper leaves are ovate.

mollis, Latin, "soft hairy."

Fragaria virginiana (34) Wild Strawberry
April–May

Habitat: open slopes, rocky hillsides, borders of woods, old fields; varied, statewide. Low, ground-hugging, roots from runners.

Flowers: clusters with 5 white petals and many stamens, typical of the Rose Family.

Leaves: 3-divided into egg-shaped, toothed lobes, on hairy stems, dark green.

Fruit: to most of us a delicious berry, to botanists an aggregate fruit.

Fragaria, Latin, "to have a scent," the classical name of strawberry.

Geum canadense (42) White Avens
May–Oct

Habitat: open woods, valleys, streamsides; statewide. Branched, 1½–2½ feet (4.5–7.5 dm) tall, stems velvety hairy.

Flowers: small, petals white, sepals green interspersed with petals, 10 or more stamens, the sepals about as long as the petals.

Rosaceae

Leaves: basal, long-petioled, often pinnate (like a feather), stem-leaves usually trifoliate with oblong, lobed, and toothed divisions. Uppermost leaves often undivided, sessile. Stipules at all nodes.

Fruit: a mass of burrlike, pointed receptacles with the dried style protruding (an achene).

Geum is the classical name of a European member of the genus.

Geum vernum Spring or Early Water Avens
April–June

Found in moist places, low woods, valleys, streamsides; statewide. Very similar to *G. canadense,* but flowers are very small, yellow, only 1/6" (½ cm) across and leaves are trifoliate with rounded, toothed divisions.

vernum, Latin, "of spring."

Gillenia stipulata (42) Indian Physic, American Ipecac
May–July

Habitat: dry uplands, open woods, usually on acid soils; central and southern Missouri. Tall, leafy, to 3 feet (9 dm) high. May cover entire hills in the Ozarks.

Flowers: in small groups arising from upper leaf axils, 5-merous, with 5 erect sepals and 5 very narrow spreading petals, about 20 stamens and 5 pistils. The petals are white.

Leaves: the basal entirely different from stem leaves, pinnately divided, fernlike. These basal leaves appear much earlier than the upright stems. Stem leaves 3-divided with lanceolate, double-toothed leaflets. All nodes have leaflike, trifoliate stipules.

"Indian physic" and "ipecac" indicate American Indian use for internal cleansing, a widespread ceremonial custom. Ipecac is an emetic derived from certain dried roots.

Gillenia, for Dr. Arnold Gillen, an obscure German physician and botanist of the 17th century; *stipulata,* Latin, "with stipules."

Physocarpus opulifolius (39) Ninebark
May–June

Habitat: moist terrain, streamsides, below bluffs; absent from northwestern Missouri. Shrub to 10 feet (3 m) tall, densely branched, often overhanging streams.

Flowers: dense, round inflorescences (somewhat like the snowball bush) with many flowers, 5 rounded petals and 5 triangular sepals, white.

Leaves: rounded to ovate, more or less 3-divided with large, irregular teeth which are sometimes blunt.

Fruit: inflated, paperlike pods (a follicle), usually 3 in a group.
Bark: splits into paper-thin layers—thus "ninebark."

> *Physocarpus,* Greek, "inflated fruit';' *opulifolius,* Latin, "with a leaf like an *opulus,*" referring to *Viburnum opulus,* which has very similar leaves.

Potentilla simplex (60) Cinquefoil
April–June

Habitat: open woods, fields, rights of way; statewide. A low plant with stems which at first are erect, but soon spread out and root at the tips.
Flowers: yellow, on long peduncles arising from a leaf node, with rounded petals interspersed by linear sepals.
Leaves: 5-divided, oblanceolate, toothed.

> *"Cinquefoil,"* French, "5 leaves."

> *Potentilla,* Latin, "little potent one," referring to the medicinal use of some of the 300 species of this genus; *simplex,* Latin, "simple," for unbranched.

Potentilla recta (66) Rough-fruited Cinquefoil
May–Aug.

Habitat: fields, pastures, waste grounds, rights of way; statewide. Native of Europe, disliked by farmers and shunned by grazing animals. Stout, leafy, very hairy, much-branched perennial to 2 feet (6 dm) tall, sometimes in large colonies.
Flowers: with 5 slightly notched petals, longer than the calyx lobes, light yellow to cream, up to 50 stamens, in flat clusters.
Leaves: 5- to 7-divided, with ovate, toothed leaflets; fingerlike. The nodes with stipules. Basal leaves on long stalk, stem-leaves on shorter stalks or stalkless.

> *recta,* Latin, abbreviation of *erecta,* "upright."

Potentilla norvegica Rough Cinquefoil
May–Oct.

Habitat: fields, waste places, roadsides; statewide. Widely distributed in Europe and possibly introduced into the United States. Usually branched, to 2 feet (6 dm) tall.
Flowers: bright yellow, arising on stalks from leaf-axils, the 5 petals and 5 sepals of about equal length.
Leaves: 3-divided, the leaflets elliptical to broadly ovate, toothed. Nodes with stipules.

> *norvegica* points to the European distribution.

Rosaceae

Prunus americana (29) Wild Plum
April–May

Habitat: borders of woods, fencerows, pastures, thickets; statewide. Shrub
or small tree conspicuous in very early spring. There are 10 other
Prunus species recorded in Missouri.
Flowers: both terminal and along woody branches in small umbels of
a few flowers, with 5 white petals.
Leaves: alternate, ovate, long-pointed, toothed with petioles.
Fruit: red, ball-shaped, about 1" (2½ cm) wide; sweet, excellent for
jellies and marmalades, but also esteemed by birds and animals.

Prunus is the classical Latin name for plum. Botanically, *Prunus*
includes plums, cherries, almonds and apricots.

Prunus serotina (29) Black Cherry, Rum Cherry
April–May

Habitat: low or upland woods, streamsides; statewide. A large tree,
50–60 feet (15–18 m) tall. Botanically a *Prunus* (plum), not a cherry.
Flowers: in dense, terminal racemes (like bottle-brush) on stems of the
current year, with many 5-petaled, small, white flowers that have
a delightful scent.
Leaves: on petioles, lanceolate to oblong, to nearly 6" (15 cm) long
with fine, incurved teeth.
Fruit: a small 1-seeded drupe (a hard stone-fruit surrounded by soft
tissue), dark blue to black; a most important food for birds.
Bark: older trees have dark brown-black scaly plates.
Wood: very valuable, similar to mahogony, used for fine furniture.

serotina, Latin, "late," because other *Prunus* species bloom earlier.

Pyrus ioensis (90) Wild Crab
April–May

(Put by some authors into the genus *Malus*.)

Habitat: open woods, borders of woods, fields, hedgerows, pastures,
streamsides; statewide. A small tree that in rare cases can attain
30 feet (9 m) and up to 18" (4.5 dm) diameter.
Flowers: large, in clusters of 3–6 along branches, deep rose-pink, pale
pink or white, with 5 petals.
Leaves: dark green above, alternate, egg-shaped to oblong, coarsely and
irregularly toothed.
Branches: with many thornlike short spurs. Leaves and flowers emerge
from the base of these spurs.
Fruit: small, green, applelike, very fragrant, greasy tasting, not desirable
for eating. Animals eat the fruit.

Pyrus, the ancient Latin name for pear; *ioensis,* Latin, "from Iowa."

Rosa: Of 15 rose species reported in Missouri, only 2 native roses have a wide distribution.

Rosa setigera (93) Prairie Rose, Climbing Rose
May–July

Habitat: moist fields, fencerows, streamsides, rights of way; statewide. Either climbs or forms sprawling thickets with arching stems.

Flowers: singly or in groups on stalks, with 5 large petals, many stamens, to 3" (8 cm) across, heavily perfumed, usually pink, rarely white.

Leaves: 3-divided on older stalks, 5-divided on recent growth; leaflets elliptical to ovate, toothed, the lateral on very short stems, the terminal on a long stem.

Rosa, classical Latin name for rose; *setigera,* Latin, "bristle-bearing," probably for the thorns.

Rosa carolina Pasture Rose
May–June

Habitat: moist places, fields, fencerows, rights of way; statewide. This is the most common *low-growing* rose with highly prickly stems (while *R. setigera* has well spaced thorns.) Height, shape of leaflets and thorniness variable.

Flowers: usually solitary, indistinguishable from *R. setigera,* pink, rarely white, very fragrant.

Leaves: compound with 3, 5 or 7 leaflets. Leaflets round, oblong or oval, small, finely toothed. The base of leaf-stem with a winged stipule.

Rosa multiflora Multiflora or Japanese Rose
May–June

Habitat: introduced and widely planted as fencerow and as an impenetrable, "living" fence. Now often escaped and a real nuisance which can only be taken out by a bulldozer. Native of Asia.

Flowers: in many-flowered inflorescences, small, white, 5-petaled.

Leaves: compound with a basal stipule, 3 or 5 leaflets which are small, obovate toothed.

multiflora, Latin, "many-flowered."

Rubus flagellaris (34) Dewberry
April–June

(Steyermark lists 16 species of *Rubus* in Missouri. Their identification is for a specialist.)

Habitat: fields, prairies, abandoned pastures, thickets, fencerows, rights of way; statewide. Dewberry is a trailing plant, rooting at the cane tips.

Flowers: in small groups, sometimes single, on long stems, white, the stems often subtended by a small leaf. Typical Rose Family flowers of 5 sepals and petals with many stamens.

Leaves: variable, mostly 3-divided, broad oval with coarse teeth. The lateral leaflets sometimes with a pointed lobe each.

Fruit: large, black berries to most of us, but aggregate drupelets to botanists, highly edible.

Rubus, Latin, from *ruber*, "red"; *flagellaris*, Latin, "whiplike."

Madder Family *Rubiaceae*

About 500 genera with 7,000 species of tropical and subtropical shrubs and trees, and mostly herbaceous plants in the temperate and arctic zones. For floral details, see page 10. Flowers of warm climate species are often much larger than those in temperate areas. Important members: coffee (*coffea*) and quinine (*Cinchona*). *Gardenia* is the best known horticultural genus. Missouri has eight genera and 24 species.

Cephalanthus occidentalis (49) Buttonbush
June–Sept.

Habitat: borders of lakes, rivers, sloughs, river bottoms; statewide. A large multi-stemmed bush, always near water.

Flowers: terminal, in ball-shaped clusters of minute 4-petaled white blossoms with protruding styles. The floral clusters arise from leaf axils.

Leaves: opposite, with petioles, ovate-oblong, to 6" (15 cm) long.

Fruit: spherical masses of pods remain for some time before splitting open. Seeds are eaten by ducks, specially wood ducks, and pheasants.

Cephalanthus, Greek, "head-flower"; *occidentalis*, Latin, "of the west."

Galium: There are 10 native species in Missouri, most of them in woodlands; they have whorled leaves, tiny white flowers in umbels and wide distribution. Early settlers used the dried, pleasantly aromatic "hay" to fill bedding.

Galium aparine (47) Bedstraw
May–July

Habitat: woods, wooded valleys, waste places, gardens, almost any shaded area; statewide. Spreading, sprawling, 4-sided stems, rarely upright.

Flowers: arise on long stems from leaf axils, white with 4 petals; in small groups, each group subtended by a few bracts.

Leaves: in whorls of 6–8, usually about 2" (5 cm) long, linear to oblanceolate. All green parts covered by coarse, recurved hairs which cling to animals and clothing.

Fruit: round, about ¼" (15 mm) across, with bristles. When dried and roasted the fruits have been used as a coffee substitute.

Galium, Greek, *gala,* "milk," as some species were used to curdle milk for cheese; *aparine,* Latin, "clinging" (see above).

Houstonia minima (106) Bluets
March–April

(Also known as *Hedyotis minima.*)

Habitat: fields, pastures, glades, floodplains, bluffs, variable; in central and southern Missouri. A tiny courier of spring, to 3" (7½ cm) high, forming mats.
Flowers: on slender stem, terminal, subtended by minute bracts, 4 petals, purple to deep violet or white with a yellow throat; always pointed skyward.
Leaves: basal only to ⅜" (1 cm) long, with a few opposite, smaller on flowering stem; linear, sessile.

The plant is an example of the confusion caused by the use of common names: some 25 different names are on record for the same dwarf bluet.

Houstonia for Dr. William Houston, a physician and botanist in Britain in the early 18th century; *minima,* Latin, "smallest."

Houstonia pusilla Bluets, Star Violet
March–April
(Also known as *Hedyotis pusilla.*)

Habitat: on acid soils of glades, dry open woods, ledges; eastern Ozarks north to St. Louis. Almost identical to *H. minima,* but taller and with deep purple or lavender flowers.

Houstonia caerulea Bluets
April–May
(Also known as *Hedyotis caerulea.*)

Habitat: in acid soils of sandstone or granite, wet meadows, sandy open woods and glades of eastern Ozarks. Slightly taller than *H. minima* and *pusilla,* with sky-blue flowers.

caerulea, Latin, "blue."

Houstonia longifolia (33) Long-leaved Houstonia
April–July
(Also known as *Hedyotis longifolia.*)

Habitat: prairies, rocky open slopes, glades, open woods, usually on acid soils but also on limestone; south of a line drawn from southwest corner of state to St. Louis. Totally different from the other *Houstonias* described. Upright, slender, branching stalks, to 8" (20 cm) high, sometimes taller, arising from a basal rosette of leaves.

Flowers: on slender stems arising from upper leaf axils, in loose or crowded cymes, minute, white, with 4 petals.

Leaves: a basal rosette; narrow, linear. Stem-leaves are opposite, linear, very short. Both types have only one central vein.

longifolia, Latin, "long-leaved" (in comparison with other *Houstonias*).

Rue Family *Rutaceae*

Mostly shrubs and trees (with a few herbs in the southern hemisphere) of about 150 genera with 900 species. Flowers generally 5-merous, with many stamens in bundles. A fleshy disk between stamens and ovary is characteristic. Fruit is a berry with a leathery cover. The genus *Citrus* (oranges, mandarines, lemons, satsumas, tangerines, limes and grapefruit) is economically important. *Dictamnus,* burning bush, is a garden plant. Missouri has two genera, each with one species.

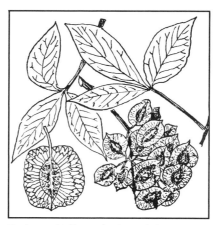

Ptelea trifoliata, fruit and leaves; actual size 2 cm.

Ptelea trifoliata (36) Hop Tree, Wafer Ash
April–June

Habitat: limestone glades, dry fields, dry hot hillsides and valleys; absent from northwestern counties. A medium-sized shrub in our area, much-branched.

Flowers: polygamous, (i.e. separate "male" and "female" flowers on the same shrub). Usually 4 sepals, petals and stamens, the petals spreading in open clusters, greenish white.

Leaves: alternate, 3-divided on long petioles, the leaflets spear-shaped without stems; leaves have an orangelike fragrance.

Fruit: a mass of flat, round, veined, papery envelopes which encircle 2 seeds; called a samara. Unripe seeds have the smell of hops and have been used as a hops substitute.

Ptelea, Greek, "elm" (similarity of fruit); *trifoliata,* Latin, "3-leaved."

Sandalwood Family *Santalaceae*

About 35 genera and 400 species of mostly parasitic herbs, shrubs and trees of tropical and temperate zones. Sepals and petals look alike, forming a tube with three or six lobes. Stamens inserted in tube opposite the lobes. Ovary inferior or semi-inferior. Sandalwood is of economic value. Other species provide oils and edible fruits. Missouri has one species.

Comandra richardsoniana (25) Bastard Toadflax
May–July

(Also known as *Comandra umbellata.*)

Habitat: dry uplands, glades, usually on acid soil; statewide except Southeast Lowlands. Usually about 1 foot (30 cm) tall, grows and flowers under the hottest conditions.
Flowers: in small groups of 5-lobed sepals emerging from a disk around the ovary; 5 stamens are inserted in the disk.
Leaves: narrow, oblong, alternate to 1½" (4 cm) long, green on both sides.
Root: sends out slender suckers which become parasitic but can persist without this feature. The "bastard" part of the common name refers to the true toadflax, a *Linaria,* which resembles *Comandra.*

Comandra, two Greek words, *comae-* and *-andros,* "man-hair," because the anthers are surrounded by tufts of hair; *richardsoniana,* for John Richardson (1787–1865) a British naturalist, botanist and explorer.

Saxifrage Family *Saxifragaceae*

Predominantly herbs of northern and alpine zones, but also shrubs and trees in warmer climates, of about 80 genera and 1,250 species. The family is closely related to the Rose Family, but never has stipules. Authors differ about what to include in the family. Leaves are often basal in a rosette. Flowers generally scapose—on leafless stems—regular, 5-merous. Fruit is a many-seeded capsule. The genus *Ribes* produces gooseberries and currants; *Hydrangeas* are cultivated. Missouri has 10 genera with 18 species, some very rare.

Saxifragaceae

Heuchera richardsonii (80) Alum Root
April–June

(Some authors combine this with *H. americana* under *H. hirsuticaulis*).

Habitat: upland rocky slopes, ledges, bluffs, rock crevices in sunny situations; statewide except Southeast Lowlands.

Flowers: on long, hairy scapes in open or dense terminal panicles. The flowers greenish, minute, tubular with stamens inserted in the tube.

Leaves: basal on long, hairy petioles, palmate, often deeply cleft with large teeth; 3-5 lobes, quite showy.

> *Heuchera* for Johann von Heucher (1677-1747), professor at Wittenberg in Germany and author on medical botany; *richardsonii,* for John Richardson (1787-1865), a British naturalist, botanist and explorer.

Hydrangea arborescens (44) Wild Hydrangea
May–July

Habitat: moist wooded hillsides, streamsides, rights of way, moist valleys, ravines, bluffs; in central and southern Missouri and the Ozarks. Shrub to 6 feet (2 m) high, spreading with light brown, brittle branches; an indicator of the presence of moisture.

Flowers: in dense, flat clusters to 5" (13 cm) across. The central flowers with 4 or 5 tiny lobes, protruding stamens are fertile. Usually there are some large, sterile flowers with 3 or 4 white lobes on the periphery; they have neither stamens nor pistils but apparently attract insects.

Leaves: on petioles, opposite, broad oval, much-toothed, green above, often pale green underneath.

> *Hydrangea,* Greek, "water-vessel" in reference to the shape of the fruit; *arborescens,* Latin, "treelike."

Ribes missouriense (30) Wild or Missouri Gooseberry
April–May

Habitat: open woods, borders of woods, wooded valleys, upland or lowlands; statewide except Southeast Lowlands. Shrub to about 3 feet (9 dm) tall, spreading as wide. The nodes from which leaves and stalk of flowers arise have from 1-3 long spines. Few prickles along stems.

Flowers: small, open, bell-shaped, with stamens and pistil protruding, hanging down, greenish to white.

Leaves: on long petioles, palmately veined with 3-5 pointed lobes with large teeth.

Fruit: matures June–September; a small berry, green or purple, tipped with the withered calyx, to ½" (13 mm) across.

There are 2 other **Ribes** species with very limited distribution in Missouri.

Ribes, probably from Danish *ribs,* the name of red currants.

Saxifraga virginiensis (23) Early Saxifrage
Feb.–June

Habitat: open, wooded slopes, rock outcroppings, ledges, glades, bluffs; usually in acid soils in Ozarks and northeast to St. Louis.
Flowers: on leafless stems (scapes); begin blooming when only 3-4"(7½–10 cm) high and continue blooming while growing to 1 foot (30 cm) high. Flowers in at first tight, later looser terminal inflorescence, with 5 white, pointed petals and 10 stamens.
Leaves: in a basal rosette, fleshy, ovate, narrowing toward base, with scalloped margins.

Saxifraga, Latin, "rock-breaker," as many species are alpine, emerging from rock cracks.

Saxifraga forbesii Swamp Saxifrage
April–June

Habitat: shaded sandstone ravines and north-facing hillsides, in acid and wet soils. Officially a rare and endangered species in Missouri, in a few localities in east-central counties; when encountered, it usually is abundant.
Flowers: on scapes to 3 feet (9 dm) tall, with wide inflorescence. The flowers green, unspectacular, very small.
Leaves: basal, to 8" (20 cm) long, ovate, the margins slightly wavy.

forbesii, for A. Forbes, a botanist from Illinois who discovered the species in 1870.

FIGWORT FAMILY *Scrophulariaceae*

About 220 genera with 3,000 species; worldwide, but centered in the north-temperate zone. Floral arrangements vary. For floral details see page 14. Foxglove (*Digitalis*) provided the original heart stimulant. Garden subjects: snapdragon, *Calceolaria*, veronica, beardstongue (*Penstemon*). Missouri has 10 genera with 18 species, some very rare.

The family and generic name, *Scrophularia*, goes back to the medieval "doctrine of signatures," which postulated that an imagined likeness between parts of the human body and those of a plant was a divine manifestation (or signature) of medicinal properties inherent in the plant to heal the similar shaped part of humans. Thus, the fleshy knobs on the rhizomes of certain figworts were supposed to heal scrofula, a tubercular disorder. Figwort was once fig-wart, a growth which was hoped could be healed by the plant.

Scrophulariaceae

Aureolaria leaves

Aureolaria pedicularia (78) Gerardia, False Foxglove
Aug.–Sept.

(Formerly known as *Gerardia pedicularia*.)

Habitat: dry, open woods, glades, in acid soils in the Ozarks. Much-branched stem, to 3 feet (9 dm) tall, hairy.

Flowers: on hairy stalks arising from upper leaf axils, long tubes with 5 lobes, light yellow to 3″ (8 cm) long, similar to the flowers of foxglove.

Leaves: opposite, pinnately divided into fernlike leaflets or small lobes (see drawing).

278

Aureolaria, Latin, "golden flower;" *pedicularia,* Latin, either "louse" or "lousy," as a European species was used in the Middle Ages to fight lice. Or possibly for the plant *Pedicularis,* which has very similar leaves.

Aureolaria grandiflora Western False Foxglove
July–Sept.

(Formerly known as *Gerardia grandiflora*).

Habitat: dry, open woods, on upper slopes and ridges of acid soils, but also on lime soils; absent from northwest and southeast Missouri. All details similar to *A. pedicularia,* but leaves deeply divided into small lobes (see drawing) without the fernlike appearance.

grandiflora, Latin, "large-flowered."

Aureolaria flava Downy False Foxglove
June–Sept.

(Formerly known as *Gerardia flava.*)

Habitat: open woods, borders of woods, glades in south and southeastern counties. All details similar to *A. pedicularia,* but the plant is NOT hairy and leaves are deeply lobed or cut into various sections (see drawing).

flava, Latin, "yellow."

Agalinis tenuifolia (105) Gerardia
Aug.–Oct.

(Formerly known as *Gerardia tenuifolia*).

Habitat: dry or moist, open woods, fields, wet and swampy areas; scattered statewide. Much-branched, bushy, to 2 feet (6 dm) tall.
Flowers: single on pedicels arising from leaf axils, light magenta to rose-purple, short tubes with 5 distinct lobes.
Leaves: opposite, with smaller leaflets growing from axils, linear, only 1¼" (3 cm) long.

Agalinis, Greek, "remarkable flax:" *tenuifolia,* Latin, "narrow-leaved."

Castilleja coccinea (89) Indian Paintbrush
April–July

Habitat: fields, prairies, glades, wet areas; statewide except northwest and Southeast Lowlands. A plant of very dry and also wet situations; variable 8–15" (20–38 cm) high, sometimes even taller. *Castilleja* may penetrate the roots of other plants and act as a parasite but does not depend on this lifestyle for survival.
Flowers: inconspicuous, greenish yellow, hidden in the axils of brilliantly colored bracts—many shades of red, orange and yellow.

Scrophulariaceae

Leaves: the basal formed during first year, short, oblong, with rounded ends. Stem-leaves alternate, sessile, narrow to linear with a fingerlike appendix. Both types very hairy.

Castilleja, for Domingo Castillejo, a Spanish botanist of the 18th century; *coccinea,* Latin, "red."

Collinsia verna (109) Blue-eyed Mary
April–June

Habitat: moist, open wooded hills or valleys, streamsides; central Missouri. A winter annual covering large areas; develops seedlings in late fall that can survive the coldest winters. About 15" (38 cm) high.
Flowers: on long stems arising from upper leaf axils, 2-lipped, the upper 2-lobed, white, the lower 3-lobed, sky-blue, rarely purple or white. The center lower lobe forms a pouch in which the stamens and the pistil are hidden.
Leaves: opposite, the lower broadly egg-shaped, slightly scalloped, on long stems; the upper nearly stemless, narrow lanceolate.

An excellent garden subject in humus-rich soil, where it will self-seed readily.

Collinsia for Zaccheus Collins, American botanist and philanthropist (1764–1831); *verna,* Latin, "in spring."

Pedicularis canadensis (56) Wood Betony, Lousewort
April–May

Habitat: open woods, shaded glades, bottomlands, streamsides, wooded valleys, in acid soils of the Ozarks. To 10" (25 cm) high when flowering but growing taller later. Often in large colonies.
Flowers: in dense terminal clusters (botanically a spike) on unbranched stalks; light yellow, 2-lipped, the upper much longer than the lower, curving over the stamens.
Leaves: basal and caudal pinnately lobed, fernlike. Basal and most stem leaves on long petioles. Each flower subtended by an oblong, leaflike bract. In early spring the emerging leaves have a beautiful wine-red color.

Lousewort, because it was believed in the Middle Ages that members of the genus had something to do with lice, either attracting or repelling them.

Pedicularis, Latin, "louse" or "lousy."

Pedicularis lanceolata Swamp Wood Betony
April–May

Habitat: moist, swampy lowlands, springfed meadows in south central and southeast counties; the common name, "wood betony," is misleading. Upright, branched, to 2½ feet (7½ dm) tall, smooth, quite different in appearance from *P. canadensis.*

Flowers: in terminal spikes, cream or yellowish white, 2-lipped, the upper much longer than the lower.
Leaves: mostly opposite, sessile or with very short petioles; lanceolate, pinnately lobed, the lobes crenately toothed.

lanceolata, Latin, "lance-shaped."

Penstemon digitalis (43) Beard Tongue
May–July

Habitat: moist borders of woods, prairies, fields, rights of way; statewide except northwest counties. The tallest of 3 white-flowered *Penstemon* in Missouri, to 4 feet (1.2 m) tall but usually lower.
Flowers: in loose terminal clusters with irregular flowers of 2 lips, the upper 2-lobed, the lower 3-lobed. Of the 5 stamens one is modified into a hairy "tongue" and positioned centrally, probably to attract insects for pollination.
Leaves: opposite, lance-shaped, sessile, widely spaced small teeth.

Penstemon, Greek, "5-stamens"; *digitalis,* Latin, "fingerlike," probably referring to the similarity of the flower to *Digitalis* (foxglove).

Penstemon pallidus Pale Beard-tongue
April–June

Habitat: dry, acid soils, borders of woods, glades, rights of way; statewide except northwest counties. Very similar to *P. digitalis,* but the flowers are off-white, it blooms earlier, and prefers dry situations.

pallidus, Latin, "pale" (the off-white color).

Penstemon tubaeflorus Funnel-form Beard-tongue
May–June

Habitat: dry, upland fields, rights of way of Ozarks and southwestern counties. Very similar to *P. digitalis* but flower clusters are narrow, the main leaves remain well below the inflorescence and have broad-margined petioles.

tubaeflorus, Latin, "with a tube-shaped flower."

Scrophularia marilandica (86) Figwort, Carpenter's Square
July–Oct.

Habitat: in rich woods, borders of woods, on slopes or in valleys; statewide. Much-branched, leafy, to 7 feet (2.1 m) tall.
Flowers: clustered terminally in open panicles that spread broadly. Individual flowers small, sacklike with a 2-lipped corolla, green outside, brown-magenta inside.

Scrophulariaceae

Leaves: lanceolate, sharply pointed, on slender petioles, opposite, with fine teeth.

Stems: 4-sided and grooved (thus Carpenter's square).

Scrophularia, see family text.

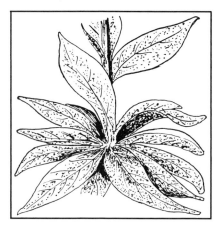

Verbascum thapsus, basal leaves; actual size 2 feet.

Verbascum thapsus (70) Mullein, Flannel Plant
May–Sept.

Habitat: dry fields, waste places, rights of way, railroad embankments; statewide. Native of Europe. This conspicuous immigrant takes over disturbed land, the stalks reaching 7 feet (2.1 m). The entire plant is densely hairy, gray.

Flowers: short, tubular with 5 yellow lobes; in a terminal, usually unbranched long spike.

Leaves: basal only during first year, the flower stalk rises during the second, the plant being a biennial. The basal leaves persist during the winter, oblong, on petioles to 1 foot (3 dm) long, extremely soft-hairy. Stem leaves progressively smaller toward top with leaf tissue continuing into the stem.

This mullein was a very early immigrant. Indians smoked the leaves; an extract against respiratory problems was used by Indians and settlers; the latter used the soft basal leaves for diapers.

Verbascum, Latin, the classical name for mullein used by Pliny; *thapsus* refers to a city in Sicily or Greece.

Verbascum blattaria (38) Moth Mullein
May–Sept.

Habitat: fields, pastures, waste places, rights of way; south of Missouri River, scattered north of it. Either single stems or much-branched, spreading stiffly at the same angle, like a partially opened umbrella, to 3 feet (9 dm) or sometimes higher.

Flowers: in loose, terminal spikes, only a few opening at one time, white or lemon-yellow, with 5 lobes and 5 red stamens. The stamens are surrounded at their base with spiderweblike hairs in violet color. With some imagination one may see a moth—thus moth mullein.

Leaves: variable, in spirals around the stem, sessile, usually oblanceolate, with or without teeth.

> *blattaria,* Latin, *blatta,* "cockroach," as the plant was supposed to discourage the pest. Another explanation of the common name is that the flowers attract moths.

Veronicastrum virginicum (48) Culver's-root
June–Sept.

Habitat: open woods, wet fields and meadows, prairies, rights of way; statewide. Tall, erect to 6 feet (1.8 m) tall with a few erect branches.

Flowers: in terminal spikes arising from a common axis, the center spike larger. Individual flowers minute, tightly spaced, a tube with 5 lobes, 2 stamens and a pistil protruding, white, rarely pink.

Leaves: smooth, in whorls, well spaced along the stalk, short-stemmed, narrow lanceolate, finely toothed.

> *Veronicastrum,* combines *veronica* and *aster.* The **Veronica** genus has very similar inflorescences. Culver's-root had medicinal applications and is named for Dr. Coulvert, an American physician of the late 17th and early 18th century.

Nightshade Family *Solanaceae*

About 90 genera with 2,500 species worldwide, but centered in Australia. For floral details, see page 12. Poisonous species are belladonna, jimsonweed, mandrake. *Nicotiana tabacum* (tobacco) is pernicious to man and nicotine extract is fatal to insects. Food plants: potato, tomato, peppers, including paprika, chillies, and pimento. Garden plants: *Nicotiana, Datura, Petunia, Salpiglossis, Schizanthus, Nierembergia, Browallia.* Deleting rarely escaped cultivated species, Missouri has four genera with 16 species.

Datura stramonium (41) Jimsonweed, Thorn Apple
May–Oct.

Habitat: pastures, barnyards, waste or cultivated land; statewide. Tall, branching, leafy, rank-smelling annual, to 5 feet (1.5 m) tall, often with purple stems. Native of tropical America.

Flowers: funnel-shaped, pleated and swirled, with 5 sharply pointed lobes, to 5" (13 cm) long. The tube emerges from a green calyx less than half the length of the corolla; white or light violet, or white with a violet throat. Flowers open in the evening with a strong perfume and close in early morning.

Solanaceae

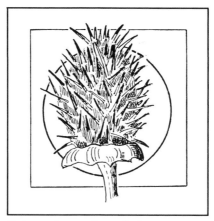

Datura stramonium, fruit;
actual size 2".

Leaves: alternate, on petioles, deeply lobed with teeth, to 4" (10 cm) long.

Fruit: ovoid, spiny capsule to 2" (5 cm) long, splitting open by 4 valves, spilling many flat, black seeds.

Like most members of the Nightshade Family, *D. stramonium* is poisonous, causing hallucinations.

Datura, Arabic or Hindustani; ***stramonium,*** Latin, of unknown meaning but also the name for dried leaves used pharmaceutically as a narcotic.

Physalis: There are 9 species in Missouri, of which the 3 below have a fairly wide distribution.

Physalis Key

1a) Mostly in moist bottomlands or near water . . . . *longifolia*
1b) Mostly in dry land, open woods, waste places . . .
   2a) leaves narrowed toward base; leaf-tissue continues into
   leaf stem (petiole) . . . . *virginiana*
   2b) leaves heart-shaped, rounded or broad at base . . . . *heterophylla*

Physalis longifolia (68) Ground Cherry
May–Sept.

Habitat: moist places, low open woods, streamsides, borders of lakes and sloughs; statewide. Erect, branched, about 2 feet (6 dm) high.

Flowers: arise singly from leaf axils, bell-shaped, sulphur yellow, about 1" (2½ cm) long.

Leaves: alternate, long petioled, either entire or with lobelike teeth, the margins of the 2 sides unsymmetrical, ovate.

Fruit: the "ground cherry," a berry in a crisp, papery husk, which is 5-sided, pointed, lanternlike.

Physalis, Greek, "bladder" (the fruit); *longifolia,* Latin, "long-leaved."

Physalis virginiana Virginia Ground Cherry
April–July

Habitat: dry, open places, waste areas, rights of way; statewide. Very similar to *P. longifolia* but stems with down-turned hair.
Leaves: narrow, pointed at both ends, the leaf-tissue often continues in to the leaf stem.

Physalis heterophylla Clammy Ground Cherry
May–Aug.

Habitat: open areas of variable habitat, uplands and low places, moist or dry; statewide except central Ozarks. Stems with sticky, spreading hairs; to 3 feet (9 dm) high.
Flowers: as for *P. longifolia* but having a purplish brown spot in their center.
Leaves: only slightly asymmetrical, egg- or heart-shaped with rounded broad base and wavy margins.

heterophylla, Greek, "various-shaped leaves."

Solanum rostratum (66) Buffalo Bur
May–Oct.

Habitat: waste places, rights of way, fields; statewide. Stems to 2 feet (6 dm) high, completely covered with sharp bristles.
Flowers: single from upper leaf axils, yellow, about 1" (2½ cm) across with 5 united petals, forming a 5-pointed star with stamens protruding. The calyx is almost concealed by bristles. Leaves alternate on spiny stems, deeply lobed almost to midrib, the main lobes further lobed.
Fruit: a globe-shaped berry entirely covered by bristles which adhere to animals.

Solanum, Latin, "quiet down," the effect of nightshade extract on the nervous system; *rostratum,* Latin, "with a beak," as one anther is elongated like a beak.

Solanum carolinense (37) Horse Nettle
May–Oct.

Habitat: as for *S. rostratum.*
Flowers: as above but petals are white to bluish purple.

Leaves: lobes somewhat resembling red oak leaves, with 4 lateral lobes and 1 terminal shallow lobe. Does NOT have bristles, but yellow prickles on stems and midribs of leaves.

Fruit: smooth, yellow berry, like a tiny tomato, which persists through the winter.

Bladder-Nut Family *Staphyleaceae*

A small family of shrubs and trees of five genera and about 60 species, mainly in the north-temperate and tropical zones. Flowers 5-merous with superior ovary, the fruit often an inflated bladder. A few are garden ornamentals. Only one genus and one species in Missouri.

Staphylea trifolia (32) American Bladder-Nut
April–May

Habitat: rich woods, on north and east-facing slopes, bluffs, streamsides, alluvial valleys; absent from Southeast Lowlands. A large shrub, very rarely a small tree, spreading from root runners.

Flowers: in small groups on a short stem arising from upper leaf axils. The flowers small, bell-shaped sepals and white petals of nearly the same length, the 5 stamens and the pistil protruding.

Leaves: trifoliate on a long stem, the lobes ovate with elongated points, the central on a distinct petiole, the lateral almost sessile, finely toothed.

Fruit: an inflated, bladderlike capsule, somewhat like a bishop's tiara but with 3 points at the bottom; encloses 1–4 light-brown seeds which rattle in the capsule.

Staphylea, Greek, "cluster" (the flowers); *trifolia*, Latin, 3-leaved.

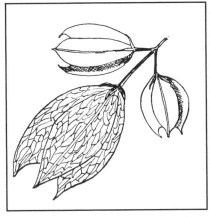

Staphylea trifolia, fruit; actual size to 3"

Nettle Family *Urticaceae*

About 45 genera with over 1,000 species of worldwide distribution, except in the coldest regions. Many species (but not all) have stinging hairs. Insignificant flowers, arising as cymes or heads from leaf axils, are unisexual. Ramie (*Boehmeria nivea*) provides valuable fiber. Missouri has five genera with six or seven species.

Laportea canadensis (50) Wood Nettle
June–Aug.

Habitat: Moist, rich, low woodlands, often in extensive stands; statewide. Single, slightly zig-zag stem, to 3 feet (1 m) tall.
Flowers: small, light green, in cymes arising from leaf axils; unisexual, staminate flowers below pistillate inflorescences.
Leaves: alternate, long petioled, broad ovate, pointed, toothed.
Stems and Leaves: covered with hairs containing caustic irritants.

"This nettle is . . . a nuisance to anyone tramping the wooded valleys in summer and autumn," Steyermark, *Flora of Missouri.*

Laportea named for Francois L. de Laporte, Count of Castelnau, entomologist in the 19th century.

Valerian Family *Valerianaceae*

Herbs and a few shrubs, mostly of the northern hemisphere but also in South America and Africa, of some 13 genera and about 400 species. Flowers are regular in our species, without sepals. In their stead they carry a ring of small appendages above the ovary. Corolla is tubular with two to four stamens inserted. The pistil consists of three united carpels of which two will abort and only one will produce seed. Leaves opposite. Members of the family produce valerianic acid, which has been used in drugs. *Valerianella* is Missouri's only genus, with four native species, three of these rare.

Valerianella radiata (25) Corn Salad
April–May

Habitat: fallow fields, waste places, rights of way; statewide except northern portion. Low herb, much-branched, usually less than 1 foot (3 dm).
Flowers: minute, in umbel-shaped, close cymes, several of these close together, forming a platform. Each flower forms a funnel with 5 white lobes.
Leaves: opposite, sessile, clasping; the lower ones with a few teeth near their base, oblong with rounded tops.

"Corn salad" because the plant can be used as salad greens.

Valerianella, Latin, "little *Valerian*"; *radiata,* Latin, "with rays," probably referring to the floral appendages mentioned in the family text above.

Vervain Family *Verbenaceae*

About 75 genera and over 3,000 species of herbs, shrubs and trees, mostly tropical and subtropical, with a few in the temperate zone. Leaves usually opposite or whorled. Flowers irregular, 4- or 5-lobed; four stamens, of which two are longer than the others. Ovary superior. *Tectona grandis* is teakwood; many other species are important sources of lumber; garden plants are: *Verbena, Lantana, Vitex,* beautyberry (*Callicarpa*) and others. Missouri has three genera and eight species, most of them verbenas.

Lippia lanceolata (45) Fog Fruit
May–Sept.

Habitat: mud and gravel margins of streams, sloughs, lakes, ditches, low meadows; statewide. Low, procumbent or ascending stems; forming large colonies.

Flowers: in small clusters, at first bell-shaped, later elongated on long stalks arising from upper leaf axils; white or light pink. The "irregular" character of the flower is hardly apparent in this species.

Leaves: opposite, spaced apart, elliptical to lanceolate, toothed.

Lippia, for August Lippi, a French traveller in the late 17th century; *lanceolata,* Latin, "lanceolate."

Verbena: The genus for which the family is named has 6 species in Missouri, all with a wide distribution. Flowers in spikes except *V. canadensis.*

Verbena Key
1a) Low, spreading plants
    2a) inflorescence flat-topped . . . . *canadensis*
    2b) flowers on short spikes . . . . *bracteata*
1b) Upright plants
    2a) leaves broadly ovate
        3a) leaves sessile . . . . *stricta*
        3b) leaves on main stem on petioles . . . . *urticifolia*
    2b) leaves narrow lanceolate . . . . *simplex*
    2c) leaves broadly lanceolate or halberd-shaped
        with long petioles . . . . *hastata*

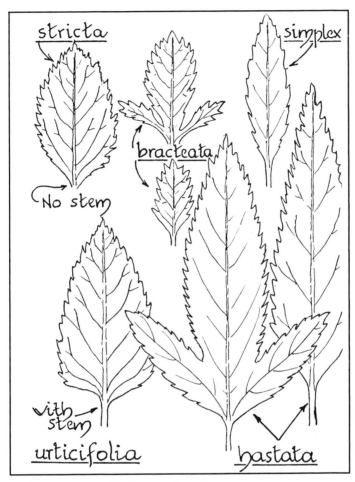

Verbena species with flowers in spikes

Verbena canadensis (87) Rose Verbena
March–Nov.

Habitat: dry hillsides, waste places, glades, borders of woods, rights of
way; statewide. Low, spreading, usually about 1 foot (3 dm) high.

Flowers: in terminal clusters, tubular with 5 lobes. Makes spectacular
displays on dry, rocky hillsides. Color varies from true pink to
magenta to rose-purple, probably depending on soil.

Leaves: variable, opposite, on petioles, more or less 3-divided with
toothed lobes, to 3'' (7½ cm) long.

Verbena, the classical Latin name of vervain.

Verbenacea

Verbena bracteata Large-Bracted Vervain
April–Oct.

Habitat: fields, waste places, rights of way; statewide. Sprawling, dwarf, very hairy with many linear bracts below the inflorescence.
Flowers: small, purplish blue, almost hidden by foliage and bracts.
Leaves: very similar to *V. canadensis*, but generally somewhat smaller.

bracteata, Latin, "with bracts."

Verbena stricta Hoary-Leaved Vervain
May–Sept.

Habitat: waste places, fields, rights of way; statewide. Erect, branched or unbranched, densely hairy, to 3½ feet (1 m) high.
Flowers: terminal in long single or multiple spikes of densely spaced flowers; corolla purple.
Leaves: sessile or nearly so, broad oval with large, irregular teeth. Leaves prominently veined beneath and densely hairy.

stricta, Latin, "erect."

Verbena urticifolia Nettle-Leaved Vervain
June–Oct.

Habitat: fallow fields, waste places, rights of way; statewide. Branched, weedy, to 6 feet (1.8 m) tall.
Flowers: on spikes, spreading stiffly like a panicle, with few flowers spaced out. The flowers are so small that they are hardly visible, though they have a white lobed corolla.
Leaves: on petioles, broadly ovate, the leaf-tissue passing into the petiole, coarsely and irregularly toothed.

urticifolia, Latin, "with a leaf of a nettle."

Verbena simplex (43) Narrow-Leaved Vervain
May–Sept.

Habitat: glades, prairies, fields, waste places, rights of way; statewide except northeast corner. Single stems or sparingly branched above, about 1½ feet (45 cm) tall.
Flowers: on single spikes with many small, deep lavender or purple flowers.
Leaves: narrow, oblong, sessile or nearly so, toothed (all other *Verbenas* treated here have broader leaves).

simplex, Latin, "simple."

Verbena hastata (116) Blue Vervain
June–Oct.

Habitat: wet places, streamsides, sloughs, lakes, waste places; absent
from Ozarks. Stems branched, rough hairs, to 5 feet (1.5 m) tall.
Flowers: in many terminal spikes, deep purple or violet, light lavender,
rarely white. The flowers open from the base of the spikes upward.
Leaves: on distinct petioles, quite variable, lanceolate to ovate, and
some with 2 lateral lobes, halberd-shaped, coarsely double-toothed,
to 5" (13 cm) long.

hastata, Latin, "spear-shaped."

Violet Family *Violaceae*

About 22 genera and 900 species, of which about 600 are of
the genus *Viola*. Cosmopolitan, but centered in the temperate zone.
Mostly herbs, a few shrubs. Flowers solitary, either regular or irregular. In the genus *Viola* the lower two petals are often enlarged,
extending into a spur which contains nectar. The five stamens are
usually fused around the variously shaped styles. Many species of
Viola also produce flowers without petals hidden under the leaves,
(cleistogamous). Pansies and violets are horticultural subjects. None
of our species is scented. Missouri has two genera with 15 species.

Hybanthus concolor (79) Green Violet
April–June

Habitat: wooded slopes, bluffs, usually on limestone; mainly south of
Missouri River. Leafy, shrublike, to 2 feet (6 dm) high, often in
large colonies.
Flowers: small, green, on short stems, curving down from leaf axils.
Sepals linear, very short; 5 petals of equal length but the lowest
petal is twice as broad as the others and swollen at its base
(gibbous). The green violet has no spur.
Leaves: many, alternate, oblong lanceolate, pointed toward both ends,
to 4½" (11.5 cm) long.
Fruit: a capsule of 3 valves that resembles a watermelon and contains
surprisingly large seeds.

Hybanthus, Greek, "hump-backed flower," the swollen base of the
lowest petal; *concolor*, Latin, "of one color" as the entire plant
is green.

Viola pedata (110) Bird's-Foot Violet, Pansy Violet, Hens
April–June   and Roosters

Habitat: rocky, well-drained, usually acid soils in open woods, road
embankments, glades, bluffs, ridges; statewide.

Violaceae

Flowers: about 1" (2½ cm) across. In 2 color phases: either all 5 petals pale lilac or lavender, or the upper 2 petals deep, velvety purple, the 3 lower pale lilac to lavender. Rare color patterns are white and combinations of the above. The center of united stamens is always deep orange.
Leaves: deeply dissected "like a bird's foot." Leaves developing later in the season have somewhat wider straplike segments.

V. pedata appreciates disturbed areas with perfect drainage but cannot survive the later intrusion of competing plants.

Viola, classical Latin name of violet; *pedata,* Latin, "footlike" (the leaves).

Viola rafinesquii (106) Johnny-jump-up
March–May

Habitat: fields, meadows, glades, rights of way, waste places, variable; absent from northern-most counties.
Flowers: very small, violet-shaped, washed-out blue with a very light yellow or white center. Plants growing on acid soils seem to have more intensive coloration.
Leaves: to ¾" (2 cm) long, rounded, irregularly scalloped, each leaf subtended by a large stipule like the spread tail of a bird.

rafinesquii for Samuel Constantine Rafinesque Schmaltz, a German botanist (1783–1840).

Blue Violets: The flowers of 7 "blue" violets (which are never blue but rather violet, purple, or lavender) are with one exception (*V. missouriensis*) so much alike that they are no help in identification. Unfortunately, leaf-shapes are often variable between early and late leaves. The drawings provided should be of some help.

BLUE VIOLETS
(with entire leaves, no deep incisions)

Viola sororia (106) Woolly Blue Violet
March–June

Habitat: open woods, borders of woods, mostly on hillsides, but also near streams and wet places; statewide. *Stems and leaves are hairy.*
Leaves: heart-shaped, scalloped, usually lower than flowers.

Viola, the classical Roman name for violet; *sororia,* Latin, "sister," because it looks so much like other violets.

Viola papilionacea Meadow Violet
March–June

Habitat: in low woods, bottomlands, generally moist areas; statewide. Nearly entirely *without hair*, otherwise just like *V. sororia*.

papilionacea, Latin, "butterflylike," possibly the flowers.

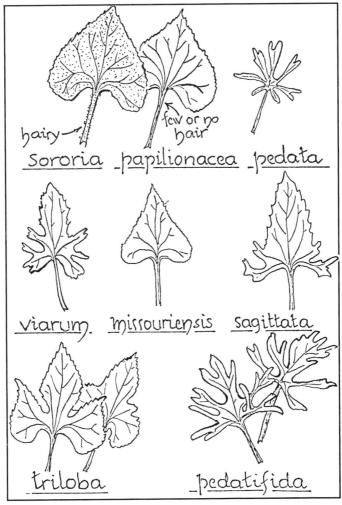

Leaves of blue or purple violets

Violaceae

Viola missouriensis Missouri Violet
March–May

Habitat: rich, moist places, bottomlands; scattered statewide. Not common.
Flowers: usually well above leaves, pale violet with a darker band around the white center.
Leaves: similar to *V. sororia,* but often more triangular and without conspicuous hair.

Viola sagittata Arrow-Leaved Violet
April–June

Habitat: in open (sunny) variable situations in a broad band from southwest to northeast Missouri.
Flowers: usually as high as the leaves.
Leaves: arrow-shaped, the two lateral basal lobes with 2 or 3 large teeth.

  sagittata, Latin, "arrow-shaped."

BLUE VIOLETS
(incised leaves)

Viola viarum Plains Violet
April–May

Habitat: moist, usually low, open places; statewide except Southeast Lowlands.
Flowers: lower than leaves.
Leaves: either entire with scalloped margins or deeply 3- to 7-lobed, the lobes coarsely toothed, or arrow-shaped with several bilateral lobes toward base of leaf.

  viarum, Latin, "of the roads."

Viola triloba Three-lobed Violet
April–May

Habitat: on acid soils in upland woods but also near streamsides; south of Missouri River and northeast counties.
Flowers: lower than leaves.
Leaves: often round and scalloped early in the season; later leaves irregularly 3-lobed, or sometimes with 5 lobes.

  triloba, Latin, "3-lobed."

Viola pedatifida Prairie Violet
April–May

Habitat: prairies of western and northern Missouri.
Flowers: somewhat larger than other violets, held slightly above foliage.
Leaves: reminiscent of *V. pedata,* but slightly wider lobes.

pedatifida, Latin, "footlike" or "palmately divided."

YELLOW VIOLET

Viola pensylvanica (55) Smooth Yellow Violet
March–May

Habitat: low woods, rich slopes, wooded floodplains; statewide. The only yellow-flowered violet in Missouri.
Flowers: on peduncles arising from upper leaf axils. The lower 3 petals have purple veining. The species begins flowering on low, small plants and keeps on flowering for a long period during which it grows up to 2 feet (6 dm) high.
Leaves: both basal and stem leaves heart-shaped with fine scalloping.

WHITE VIOLETS
(Besides V. striata, below, there are 2 other white violets in Missouri, both rare.)

Viola striata Striped Violet
April–June

Habitat: moist, open woods and bottomlands; absent from northern and western counties. Starts flowering low to ground. As season progresses, flowers become smaller and smaller and the plant grows to nearly 2 feet (6 dm) high.
Flowers: white or cream-white, the lowest petal with a few purple stripes.
Leaves: both basal and stem heart-shaped, with fine scalloping.

striata, Latin, "striped," see above.

Grape Family *Vitaceae*

Climbers and some shrubs, of tropical, subtropical and temperate zones, of 12 genera with about 700 species. Most are climbers with tendrils. Flowers minute in cymes or racemes, sepals fused four or five, petals also four or five, stamens as many as petals, ovary superior. *Vitis vinifera,* grapevine, came from the Orient or India. Missouri has four genera and 13 species.

Vitaceae

Vitis: There are eight species of grape in Missouri, five with wide distribution. *Vitis vulpina* was chosen as example. The species vary mainly in leaf-shapes.

Vitis vulpina (82) Frost or Chicken Grape
May–June

Habitat: Low, moist woods, wooded bottomlands, streamsides; statewide except Southeast Lowlands. Rampant climber with stout, woody stems.

Flowers: in long, slender panicles, light green, scented.

Leaves: rounded with or without 3 lobes, coarsely toothed, to 8" (20 cm) long.

Fruit: the grapes become sweet only after frost and are eaten by birds and mammals.

Vitis, the classical Latin name for grape; **vulpina,** Latin, "little fox," as Br'er Fox loves grapes.

Glossary

Achene—a dry, single-celled, one-seeded fruit which does not split open.

Acicular—see "leaf shapes," page 7.

Alternate—see "leaf positions," page 6.

Angiosperm—plants with true flowers, their ovules enclosed in a carpel.

Anther—the pollen-bearing part of the stamen.

Arrow-shaped—see "leaf shapes," page 7.

Awl-shaped—see "leaf shapes," page 7.

Basal—arising directly from the ground, or the leaves at the base of a stalk.

Basal rosette—basal leaves more or less arranged as a rosette.

Berry—fruit having its seeds embedded in fleshy or pulpy material.

Blade—surface of a leaf, see "simple leaf," page 6.

Bract—small, modified leaflets subtending an inflorescence or flower. See page 151.

Bulb—usually a rounded, underground structure of overlapping bases of leaves, a storage facility.

Calyx—collectively, the sepals or outer perianth (Greek, "around the flower").

Carpel—the ovule-bearing structure of a flower.

Caudal—leaf emerging from a plant stalk.

Chaff—small, thin scale, specifically the bract subtending the florets of many composites.

Clasping—base of leaf surrounds stem partially or fully.

Claw—narrow, stalklike base of some sepals and petals.

Cleistogamous—self-pollinating flower which does not open.

Column—fused structure of stamens and carpels in orchids.

Compound—leaf divided into separate leaflets, see "compound leaves," page 6.

Cordate—see "leaf shapes," page 7.

Corm—enlarged, fleshy, subterranean part of stem; solid; a storage facility.

Corolla—collectively, the petals, either distinct or fused (Latin, "little crown").

Corona—appendages between the corolla and the stamens. See *Silene virginica* and *Asclepias* (Latin, "crown").

Corymb—see page 5.

Cotyledon—see "seed-leaf."

Crenate—see "leaf margins," page 7.

Cuneate—see "leaf shapes," page 7.

Cyathium—see page 16.

Decompound—more than once compound or divided, see "compound leaves," page 6.

Deltoid—see "leaf shapes," page 7.

Dentate—see "leaf margins," page 7.

Dicotyledon—plant with 2 seed-leaves.

Dimorphic—occurring in 2 forms.

Dioecious—staminate and pistillate flowers on different plants of the same species.

Disk flower—tubular flowers or florets in the center of flower-heads of the composites.

Distinct—any floral organ which is not joined to another.

Drupe—stony, single seed surrounded by fleshy tissue and an outer skin (cherry, peach, plum).

Eared—lower part of leaf forming 2 earlike lobes.

Entire—see "leaf margins," page 7.

Falls—see "Iris," page 11.

Family—the class above the genus in the classification of plants.

"Female" flower—correctly, a pistillate flower, unisexual, without functional "male" parts (stamens).

Fertile—capable of producing viable seeds.

Filament—stalk of a stamen, see page 8.

Floret—small flower, often densely grouped, as in composites.

Floriferous—having many flowers (Latin, "bearing flowers.")

Flower—the seed-producing structure of a flowering plant. It may have individual sepals and petals, or may be in a tubular shape with or without lobes indicating the petals and sepals.

Follicle—fruit of one carpel, which splits open on one side.

Fruit—seed-bearing part of plant.

Fused—joined floral parts, as sepals, petals, stamens.

Genus—group of closely related plants; in classification, the class above the species.

Glomerule—compactly clustered flowers.

Gynophore—stalk carrying an ovary, see *Euphorbia,* page 16.

Gynostemium—compound structure of stamens and pistil(s) by adnation (the union of unlike parts), see page 146, 5.

Habitat—environment of a specific plant or group of plants.

Halbert-shaped—see "leaf shapes," page 7.

Hastata—see "leaf shapes," page 7.

Heart-shaped—see "leaf shapes," page 7.

Herb—non-woody plant.

Herbaceous—like an herb.

Heterostyly—species with flowers having styles of different length.

Hypanthium—cup-shaped, enlarged floral receptacle or the base of floral parts; often surrounds the fruits.

Inflorescence—floral structure with a definitive arrangement of flowers.

Involucre—collectively, the bracts surrounding an inflorescence.

Lanceolate—see "leaf shapes," page 7.

Lance-shaped—see "leaf shapes," page 7.

Ligulate—straplike, floral parts or leaves. Applied to certain flowers of the Composite Family; (*ligulum*, Latin, "strap.")

Linear—see "leaf shapes," page 7.

Lip—1) upper and lower sections of flowers of Mint Family (*Lamiaceae*) 2) lower petal of certain orchids, the labellum forming a pouch (Latin, "lip").

Lobe—1) terminal divisions of fused flowers 2) rounded margins of leaves, see "leaf margins," page 7.

"Male" flower—correctly, a staminate flower, unisexual, without functional "female" parts (pistil, ovary).

Margin—edge of a leaf, see "leaf margins," page 7.

-Merous—suffix indicating the number of floral parts, e.g. a 3-merous flower has floral parts in threes or multiples thereof, page 8.

Monocotyledon—plants with only one seed-leaf.

Needle-shaped—see "leaf shapes," page 7.

Node—location on a stem where a leaf or branch emerges.

Oblong—see "leaf shapes," page 7.

Opposite—see "leaf positions," page 6.

Ovary—part of pistil containing the egg or eggs; (Latin, "small egg(s)"). See "parts of a flower," page 8.

Ovary position—perianth below ovary—superior; perianth inserted above ovary—inferior; perianth around ovary—perigynous; (Greek, "around the female").

Ovate—see "leaf shapes," page 7.

Palmate—see "leaf margins," page 7.

Panicle—see "arrangement of inflorescences," page 5.

Pappus—modified calyx of composites, consisting of bristles, hairs, scales, or awns. See page 151.

Parasite—a plant that obtains nourishment from a host plant.

Parasitic—like a parasite.

Parthenogenic—development of a new plant from seed which has not been fertilized. (Greek, "virgin birth").

Pedicel—stalk of an individual flower in an inflorescence.

Peduncle—stalk of a single flower of an inflorescence.

Perfect flower—having both staminate and pistillate functional parts in the same flower.

Perfoliate—base of leaf or petiole completely surrounding the stem.

Perianth—collectively, the calyx and the corolla. (Greek, "around the flower").

Petal—a distinct part of the corolla.

Petaloid—applied to sepals, acting like petals, when petals are missing. (Greek, "like a petal").

Petiole—stem of leaf; the leaf stalk.

Pinnate—either veining or shape of leaf, see "leaf veining," page 6 and "leaf margins," page 7. (Latin, *pinna* "feather").

Pinnatifid—pinnately incised or divided.

Pinnules—secondary division of a pinnate leaf.

Pistillate—see "female flower."

Plaited—longitudinal folds.

Plicate—Latin, "plaited."

Pollen—collectively, the pollen grains contained in the anther.

Pollinium—waxy, coherent mass of pollen grains, as in *Asclepias* and Orchids.

Polygamous—plant with both perfect and imperfect flowers.

Raceme—see page 5.

Radial symmetry—see "regular flower."

Rayflower—outer or ligulate (Latin, "straplike"), flowers formed around the disk of many composites.

Receptacle—more or less enlarged base of a flower or inflorescence.

Regular flower—having "radial symmetry," i.e. can be halved at any angle to form two identical halves, see page 8.

Rhizome—underground, more or less horizontal stem, thickened to store water and nutrients.

Sagittate—see "leaf shapes," page 7. (Latin, *sagitta* "arrow").

Saprophyte—plant obtaining food from non-living organic matter.

Scape—leafless stalk, arising from ground, with flowers either carried terminally or along the scape.

Scapose—a plant having a scape.

Seed—ripened egg.

Seed-leaf—one or two small leaves developing from the sprouting seed, botanically "cotyledon," (Greek, "stage shoes").

Sepal—distinct part of the calyx.

Serrate—see "leaf margins," page 7. (Latin, *serra,* "saw").

Simple leaf—one blade, in contrast to a compound leaf; see "simple leaf," page 6.

Spadix—floral spike on a fleshy stem with very small flowers enveloped by a sheath, typical of the *Araceae.*

Spath—sheath enveloping the spadix.

Spatulate—see "leaf shapes," page 7.

Species—similar plants producing through interbreeding viable seeds and new generations resembling the parent plants to a high degree. (No generally accepted definition exists.)

Spike—see "arrangement of inflorescences," page 5.

Spoon-shaped—see "leaf shapes," page 7, number 7.

Spur—1) in flowers, a modified petal or sepal forming an elongated tube containing nectar, as in *Delphinium* and violet. 2) on woody stems, growth resembling a thorn, but not pointed.

Stamen—"male," pollen-producing part of flower, see "parts of flower," page 8.

Staminate—see "male flower."

Staminode—sterile stamen or structure resembling a stamen.

Standard—1) Pea Family, the top petal of the subfamily *Papilionaceae*. 2) Iris Family, the erect part of the perianth.

Sterile—unable to produce viable seed.

Stigma—part of the pistil which receives the pollen.

Stipule—small to fairly large appendage at the base of a petiole, often leaflike, but also scales or spines.

Stolon—runner or any horizontal stem disposed to root from the nodes.

Style—connecting portion of the pistil between stigma and ovary; see "parts of a flower," page 8.

Subulate—see "leaf shapes," page 7.

Succulent—fleshy, water-holding.

Taproot—main root, usually vertical, from which secondary, lateral roots emerge.

Tepal—Sepals and petals entirely or nearly alike.

Terminal—on the top of a stalk, (Latin, the "apex").

Ternate—see "compound leaves," page 6.

Translator—see page 146, (*Asclepias*).

Triangular—see "leaf shapes," page 7.

Tri-foliate—see "compound leaves," page 6, (Latin, "three-leaved").

Tube—tubular-joined sepals and/or petals.

Tuber—thickened short branch, growing underground, bearing buds and "eyes."

Twice Pinnate—see "compound leaves," page 6.

Umbel—see "arrangement of flowers," page 5; a "simple" umbel is a inflorescence with only one point from which the pedicels arise. If a number of small umbels are connected by stalks to a central focal point, the umbel is compound.

Undulate—see "leaf margins," page 6.

Veining—vascular bundles form a network for the transport of liquids to and from the leaf; see "leaf veining," page 6.

Wings—the 2 lateral petals of flowers of the subfamily *Papilionaceae* of the pea-family, see page 8.

Whorled—see "leaf positions," page 6.

Index

302